AN ELECTRON MICROGRAPHIC ATLAS OF VIRUSES

AN ELECTRON MICROGRAPHIC ATLAS OF VIRUSES

By

ROBLEY C. WILLIAMS

Department of Molecular Biology and Virus Laboratory

University of California

Berkeley, California

and

HAROLD W. FISHER

Department of Microbiology and Biophysics

University of Rhode Island

Kingston, Rhode Island

CHARLES C THOMAS · PUBLISHER

Springfield · Illinois · U.S.A.

Published and Distributed Throughout the World by

CHARLES C THOMAS • PUBLISHER

Bannerstone House

301-327 East Lawrence Avenue, Springfield, Illinois, U.S.A.

©*1974, by* CHARLES C THOMAS • PUBLISHER

ISBN 0-398-03153-3

Library of Congress Catalog Card Number: 74-2180

Library of Congress Cataloging in Publication Data

Williams, Robley Cook, 1908–
    An electron micrographic atlas of viruses.

    Bibliography: p.
    1. Viruses—Atlases. I. Fisher, Harold W., joint authors. II. Title. [DNLM:
1. Microscopy, Electron—Atlases. 2. Viruses—Atlases. QW17 W726e 1974]
QR363.W54   576'.64'0222   74-2180
ISBN 0-398-03153-3

Printed in the United States of America

CC-11

To Margery and Doris

PREFACE

About three years ago we developed a technique that allowed virus particles to be photographed in the electron microscope without subjecting them to the heavy electron irradiation which they undergo during traditional electron microscopy. The first results, obtained on bacteriophage T4 and tobacco mosaic virus, showed that the method allowed discernment of details of structure that were finer than any previously shown. We then began to examine other viruses available from our colleagues in the Virus Laboratory, and fairly soon we had a respectable collection of electron micrographs. It occurred to us that others interested in the structure of viruses might wish to see our photographs, particularly if we could enlarge the collection to include examples of viruses of many known structural types. Thanks to the generosity of colleagues in many places, who gave us samples of viruses which we did not have, we have been able to assemble an *Atlas* containing electron micrographs of some thirty-one different viruses.

The *Atlas* is intended for two classes of people: those who are investigators in virus research and who would find it useful, in either their research or teaching, to have available a fairly extensive collection of electron micrographs; and those whose interest in viruses is secondary, or just beginning, but who would like to learn more about their visual appearance. The brief accounts accompanying the Plates in the *Atlas* are intended for the latter audience, since they are not intended to be extensive nor highly technical. We hope that, in examining the micrographs in this *Atlas* the reader will be struck, as we are, by the fantastically diverse ways in which Nature has assembled large molecules into ordered structures.

All of the electron micrographs in the *Atlas* were obtained by one or the other of us in the senior author's laboratory, and all were obtained by use of the technique of minimal electron beam exposure (Williams, R. C., and Fisher, H. W., *J Mol Biol, 52:* 121, 1970). Most of them were photographed at the initial magnification of × 40,000, either in a Siemens 1A or a JEOL 100B electron microscope, both equipped with anticontamination devices. The support films for specimen deposition were carbon over collodion; negative staining was almost always by use of sodium phosphotungstate. Photographic enlargements were on Eastman bromide paper, grades F-3 to F-5. The magnifications at which the micrographs are presented are not uniform; rather, each picture is at a magnification only great enough to show the smallest detail of structure which is unequivocally present.

The arrangement of the thirty-one micrographs in the *Atlas* is based upon the considerations discussed in the Introduction and shown in its accompanying chart. At the beginning of the account accompanying each Plate is a very brief description of the chemical and physical properties of the virus: the type and strandedness of the nucleic acid and its percentage content, the shape of the virus particle and whether it is naked or enveloped, and its dimensions.

ROBLEY C. WILLIAMS
HAROLD W. FISHER

INTRODUCTION

Background

Ever since the discovery in 1935 that the virus of the mosaic disease of tobacco was a chemically defined macromolecule, rather than a mysterious living substance, the elucidation of virus structure has been the subject of much study. For several years, however, the small size of viruses precluded attempts at their direct visualization by optical means, and limited the structural investigations to determinations of their sizes and shapes by physical methods such as ultrafiltration, sedimentation and diffusion analysis, and viscometry. Only the pox viruses were large enough to be seen by bright-field, light microscopy. Dark-field microscopy was capable of revealing objects believed to be the particles of the smaller viruses, but such imagery could establish only imprecise estimates of shapes and sizes. At the close of the 1930's our knowledge of virus structure was limited to the realization that several viruses were approximately isometric, with diameters covering a range from 15 nm to 150 nm, and that one, tobacco mosaic virus, was rod-shaped with a length, approximately 300 nm, about twenty times its diameter. Nothing was known about any finer scale structure. With the advent of the electron microscope the exploration of the physical properties of viruses changed dramatically. In 1939 the first electron micrographs of viruses were obtained, showing that, indeed, tobacco mosaic virus was a rod, that other viruses showed images interpretable as arising from spheres, and that still other viruses looked like tadpoles. While these first pictures were not even second-class by present standards, they did afford exciting promise that the electron microscope would eventually be a powerful instrument in delineating virus structure.

The word *structure* as applied to objects the size of viruses may mean different things to different investigators. An analytical chemist may say that he knows the structure of a protein molecule if he has determined the sequence of its amino acid residues. The physical biochemist may be primarily interested in size, shape, density, and water of hydration of such a molecule, with its distribution of electric charge included for good measure. An x-ray analyst wants the three-dimensional localization of the atomic scattering centers within the molecule when it is part of a crystalline assembly, but must remain content to be relatively ignorant, from his own work, of the chemical identity of the scattering centers. The electron microscopist seeks information similar to that found by the x-ray analyst. His methods have certain advantages and disadvantages. He starts with the supposition that a virus particle does not consist of material which has a uniform density over all the volume occupied by the particle; that there are regions from which water is highly excluded and regions consisting mostly of water, and that even within the former regions the density may vary because of differences of chemical composition. These local differences in density constitute his *structure* of the particle. The actual specimen examined is a single particle, hopefully treated to accentuate the differences in water content and chemical composition, and it must be photographed after it has dried from its normal environment. Since all the optical information comes from single particles the problem of distinguishing signal from noise is severe, and since the photographs are two-dimensional projections of three-dimensional objects oriented at random the problems of interpretation are not simple.

While in principle the electron microscope will resolve details in the near-atomic size range, as does x-ray analysis, in practice the resolution limit in electron micrographs of viruses is not nearly so fine. The x-ray analyst uses a crystal as a specimen; consequently he is presented with the redundancy of information arising from a periodic arrangement of structure and is able to enhance notably the signal-to-noise ratio. By use of computational methods the structural information can be presented in three-dimensional form at a high level of resolving power. But x-ray analysis of this nature is restricted to objects that will crystallize and are relatively simple in structure, and it is laborious and time-consuming. On the other hand, electron microscopy will yield some information about any object within its workable size range, whether or not the particle is crystallizable, and the application of its methods, while requiring skill and judgment, does not take much time. The methods of x-ray analysis and electron microscopy are complementary rather than competitive.

Specimen Preparation

An electron micrograph of a particle like a virus that has simply been allowed to dry out of its aqueous environment is unimpressive. The contrast in the image is low, evidence of inner structure is not usually present, and the object appears obviously flattened by the forces of surface tension during drying. Even though the electron microscope has ample resolving power to show fine detail, there is no evidence of that capability in the micrograph. Almost all the improvements in the practical micrography of purified virus particles have been directed toward the problems of contrast and preservation of three-dimensional structure of the specimen. Contrast in the image of an untreated virus particle is poor because the electrons passing through different portions of it are all scattered to about the same degree; i.e. in a dried particle of organic material every electron traverses about the same mass of material. Contrast would be improved if certain regions of the particle, related to its external or internal structure, could be stained with a substance of high density (high electron scattering power). The first staining of this nature, a surface *stain*, was accomplished by the shadowing technique, introduced in 1944. A thin film of a heavy metal, such as uranium, was vacuum-deposited at an oblique angle upon the dried virus particles, thus creating variations in the thickness of the film wherever the particle surface had humps and hollows. Regions of thicker or thinner metal film introduced more or less electron scattering, resulting in greatly enhanced contrast based upon surface topology. While the results were striking, and while the technique had universal application for about fifteen years, it always suffered from three defects: It did nothing to alleviate the artifacts of drying, it obscured whatever inner structure might be present, and it produced a fine-scale granulation on the particle surface because of the crystallite structure of the metal film.

In the early 1950's two successful methods were developed for preventing the artifacts that come about when virus particles dry out of water. In one, the *critical point* method, the specimen is transferred from a water solution to a solvent that is miscible in both water and liquid CO_2, at high pressure and room temperature. The pressure is then reduced and the specimen dries from a gaseous environment; thus, no water-air interface passes over it. The other method was simply an application of freeze-drying to electron microscopy, wherein the specimen is dried out of an ice matrix upon vacuum sublimation at low temperature.

During most of the years in which the shadowing method was extensively used for revealing the surface structure of virus particles little serious attention was given to the development of chemical stains for this purpose. It was recognized that the large gamut of stains available to light microscopy would not be applicable to electron microscopy, since these stains act by the selective absorption of certain regions of the visible spectrum, thereby providing differentiation of stained structures by their differences of color. The only staining effect that can be observed in the electron microscope is one that is brought about by differences of mass per unit area of the specimen that is traversed by the electrons. This fact requires that good electron stains be compounds of heavy metals such as tungsten and uranium, if the volume occupied by the stain is to be kept at a desirable minimum. With this restriction it could not be expected that stains with a high degree of chemical specificity could be found, as distinct from the situation in light microscopy.

In 1959 a highly successful technique was developed for enhancing the contrast in images of particles, such as viruses, by the use of heavy metal salts. The method was called *negative staining*, although a more apt description is *heavy metal embedding*. The process is the essence of simplicity: An aqueous suspension of virus particles is mixed in equal volume with a 1 to 4 percent solution of a heavy metal salt, such as sodium phosphotungstate (PTA), and the mixture allowed to dry on the electron microscope specimen film. The dried specimen consists of virus particles embedded in the residue of the stain that remains after drying. Wherever the particle has a hollow region, or a surface indentation, initially filled with water, it will now contain a mass of stain. Wherever there is a protuberance there will be less stain. Electrons passing through the hollow or indented regions will experience more scattering, because of the local mass of dried stain, than will electrons traversing a region where there is a surface protuberance. Thus, the electron image will have areas that are relatively dark and light, corresponding to regions in the particle that are relatively thin and thick, as seen by the traversing electrons. The contrast is thus inverse; thick specimen areas appear electron lucent and thin areas appear relatively electron opaque. This effect was the origin of the term *negative stain*. Since a very thin film of a dense material such as

PTA will create a notable enhancement of electron scattering, the power of this method to delineate very small structural differences is great.

An unanticipated, but enormous, benefit of the method of negative staining lies in its relatively good preservation of three-dimensional structure during drying of a virus particle. As water is removed the space occupied by it is filled with a matrix of stain which becomes progressively harder as drying proceeds. Thus, the particle cannot greatly flatten and distort during preparation for electron microscopy. It is safe to say that negative staining has gone far to solve two problems of specimen preparation at one blow: introduction of fine-scale contrast in the electron image, and preservation of structure during drying.

The virtue of negative staining, that it discloses structure in any part of a particle accessible to the stain, also produces a disadvantage in the interpretation of micrographs. Suppose a virus particle has protuberances all over its surface. The stain will enter the hollows between the protuberances regardless of whether they lie on the part of the virus surface that is *below* (next to the specimen film) or *above* (farthest from the film). In addition, some stain may enter the interior of the particle. Since the electron image is a two-dimensional projection of all the structural details on and within the particle, as revealed by the negative stain, its interpretation may be far from straightforward. Recently, stereoscopic micrographs (obtained by tilting the specimen between two successive photographic exposures) have been used to help unscramble the puzzle of overlapping regions of contrast.

The general method of negative staining described above occasionally requires modification in actual practice, and it may not always produce ideal results. Each stain used has a limited pH range, and the virus sample may suffer some structural degradation at pH's within this range. Some viruses are not stable in pure water and must be kept in an ionic solution. If the necessary solute is fairly concentrated and is nonvolatile, and is present when the negative stain is added, it may create a coarse granulation in the dried negative stain. A solution to this dilemma is to dialyze the virus sample into a volatile buffer, such as ammonium acetate or ammonium bicarbonate, at an appropriate pH and ionic strength. Another problem has to do with uneven spreading of the virus-containing negative stain upon the specimen film. If the virus concentration is low ($\approx < 10^{12}$ particles/ml), the stain tends to dry in patches that are either too thick or too thin to be useful. One way to minimize this problem is to add material that will aid uniform spreading. Some of the Plates in this *Atlas* (such as Plate VIII) show particles of potato virus X as well as the virus of interest; the long, sinuous particles of potato virus X were added to help create a uniform film of dried stain. More recently it has been found that if the carbon specimen-support film is treated to a high-voltage glow discharge in a partial vacuum it will be rendered quite hydrophilic and uniform staining will result. Many of the following Plates are micrographs obtained after treatment of the support films in this manner.

One last problem in specimen preparation is the tendency of the particles of some viruses to flatten and partially disintegrate upon even the gentlest drying in negative stain. The herpes simplex virus (Plate XXVI) is an example of this extreme fragility. The disintegration of virus particles during drying can be informative since sometimes internal structures are best revealed after partial disruption (Plate V, Sendai virus) .

It has been recognized only recently that the procedures involved in the actual electron micrography of a particle as small as a virus may be quite damaging to its finest details of structure. Traditional electron microscopy involves using the actual virus particles which are to be photographed as the reference objects during focusing of the electron image on the viewing screen. The attendant exposure of the particles to a fairly intense beam apparently volatilizes some of the material of the virus and even rearranges the distribution of negative stain. Fortunately, it is possible to minimize the damaging effect of the electron beam by use of a portion of the specimen near the region of interest for performing the operations of focusing, leaving the important region unirradiated until the instant the photograph is taken. This technique has been called *minimal beam exposure;* it has been used in obtaining all the electron micrographs in this *Atlas.*

Principles of Virus Structure

Prior to about 1955 there was little thought given to whether viruses in general had any regularity of structure, any evidence that they were built on architectural plans. To be sure, x-ray analysis of tobacco mosaic virus had strongly intimated that its structure was that of a helix, electron micrographs of some small, freeze-dried viruses showed them to have an hexagonal outline, and the surface of rabbit papilloma virus was known to exhibit protuberances in a regular array. But so far as most viruses were concerned, they were known by the chemist to consist of protein and nucleic acid, with occasionally some lipid, and were recognized by the electron microscopist only to be particles which were frequently uniform in size and were shaped like bricks, spheres, rods, or tadpoles.

With the acceptance of the notion of RNA-protein translational coding a new way of looking at virus structure was inevitable. The genomes of many viruses clearly contained so little coding capacity that the proteins of their coats could not be made up of molecules larger than about 50,000 daltons. Some viral proteins had been analyzed and found to be in this range of molecular weight. Since the total amount of protein in the coat of even a small virus was at least 3 to 4×10^6 daltons, it became evident that the entire coat protein must consist of multiple copies of smaller units. Furthermore, x-ray analysis of crystals of two small, spherical viruses had shown that the particles were built with exquisite symmetry, an indication of a highly organized physical structure. Shortly after the introduction of negative staining there were increasing reports of regularly arrayed structures on the surfaces of virus particles. The time was ripe to devise a model system of construction, a set of architectural principles, hopefully for all viruses.

A puzzling aspect of the early micrographs showing regular surface structures on virus particles was that, in those cases where the number of protuberances could be calculated from the micrographs, it always ended in the number *2;* e.g., 12, 32, 42···252··. Various schemes were postulated to account for this numerology, but in 1962 Caspar and Klug uncovered the principles upon which the protein coats of virus particles, at least the simpler ones, are built, and from these principles the magic number *2* lost its element of mystery. They started with the observation that the simpler viruses, except for the tailed bacteriophage, are either rod-shaped or isometric. In the former case, the principle of construction is simple: The particles are built with helical symmetry, since this is an arrangement that would impart minimal energy to an aggregate of identical protein molecules bound in strictly equivalent positions to other such molecules and to the nucleic acid polymer. For isometric particles the minimal energy state is met if all the protein subunits are in equivalent positions; i.e. each subunit is bound to its neighbors exactly like every other subunit. It could be shown that an isometric form would result only when there were 60n such subunits; it would then have the symmetry elements of an icosahedron. (Icosahedral symmetry is also known as 5 3 2 symmetry, meaning that axes of 5-fold, 3-fold, and 2-fold symmetry may be passed through the center of the particle.) Such symmetry seemed reasonable as a principle of construction, since the earlier x-ray work had shown intimations of 5 3 2 symmetry in small virus particles.

At this stage the theory of Caspar and Klug would not explain the mysterious number *2,* nor why some viruses like adenovirus (Plate XXIV) showed angular contours and planar facets. An isometric shell built with 60n subunits in equivalent bonding positions would be expected to exhibit a circular contour. This dilemma led to the concept of quasi-equivalence: bonding which is almost identical for every subunit. With only small energy increments due to strain distortion an isometric object can be built of subunits, having icosahedral symmetry and having the observed planar facets; in the extreme the object would actually be an icosahedron, like adenovirus. Next came the notion of clustering of the protein subunits. There is no energetic reason why groups of subunits could not cluster; the only problem was to devise a clustering that would be in accord with the electron microscope results (12, 32··252 visible protuberances). It could be shown that clustering of the subunits into dimers, trimers, pentamers, and hexamers would satisfy the symmetry requirements. It actually turns out that pentamer-hexamer clustering is by far the most common, only tomato bushy stunt virus (Plate XII) having been found to have a different clustering, the dimer.

The regular array of protein, or structural, subunits forming the closed shell of a virus particle is called its *capsid,* and, as noted above, the array may have either helical or icosahedral symmetry. The structure that is composed of the capsid and its enclosed nucleic acid is called the *nucleocapsid.* The simplest capsid of an isometric virus would have 60 structural subunits. These would cluster around the 12 vertices of the equivalent icosahedron. Such a particle (the *virion* of the virus) would appear to have 12 visible protuberances, or morphological units, or *capsomers.* Elaborations beyond this primitive arrangement are most readily understood if it is imagined that the structural units are arrayed on the surface of a polyhedron that is either an icosahedron or a pentagonal dodecahedron. (They may not be actually arrayed on such a surface, but their symmetry would still be 5 3 2.)

An icosahedron is a polyhedron built of 20 identical, equilateral triangles, having 12 vertices and 30 edges. The dodecahedron is a polyhedron built of 12 identical pentagons, having 20 vertices and 30 edges. While virions are known that are built on the dodecahedron as the base, the elaboration of capsomeric structure is easiest seen with the icosahedron. The 12-capsomer virion may be thought of as having three identically spaced protein subunits per triangle of the icosahedron; 60 subunits in all, clustered as pentamers near the 12 vertices. But each of the 20 triangular facets of an icosahedron can be divided into equilateral sub-triangles whose number, T, is given by $T = Pf^2$, where $P = 1$ and $f = 1, 2, 3 \cdots$. In the case of the icosahedron, T (the *triangulation number*) is thus 1, 4, 9 $\cdots$. Each sub-triangle must contain three subunits in identical, equal-spaced array. The entire capsid of a $T = 4$ capsid would then contain 240 subunits $(20 \times 3 \times 4)$. Those nearest the 12 vertices will cluster into pentamers. The remaining 180 (240 *minus* 60) subunits can cluster into a regular array of hexamers, giving the entire capsid a surface studded with $12 + 180/6 = 42$ capsomers in regular array. When $T = 9$ the number of capsomers will be 92; $T = 16$ gives 162, etc. Thus, with pentamer and hexamer clustering, the number of units observable in the electron microscope, the capsomers, will always end in *2*, since the number of pentamer clusters will be 12 and the number of hexamers will be a multiple of 10. Figures 1 and 2 show models of an icosahedron upon which structural subunits and capsomers have been drawn for the cases of $T = 1$ and $T = 3$.

If the basic polyhedron is the pentagonal dodecahedron the equation $T = Pf^2$ still applies, but now $P = 3$. Hence T takes on the values 3, 12, 27 $\cdots$, and if the subunit clustering is pentamer-hexamer the number of observable capsomers will be 32, 122, 272 $\cdots$.

Capsid arrangements falling into neither the $P = 1$ or $P = 3$ class may exist. Closed structural shells with 5 3 2 symmetry, in which the

Figure 1. Model of an icosahedron upon which has been sketched circles to show structural subunits of the *capsid*, and connected circles to show clustering of the subunits. In this, the $T = 1$ arrangement, the 60 subunits cluster in pentagonal array at the icosahedral vertices.

Figure 2. Same as Figure 1, except that the $T = 4$ arrangement is illustrated. Spots drawn on the model show location of structural subunits in hexagonal clustering with pentagonal clustering at the vertices.

subunit bonding is quasi-equivalent, can be constructed with any value of T that is given by the relation $T = Pf^2$. While the two smallest values of P are 1 and 3, as mentioned above, the general expression for P is $P = h^2 + hk + k^2$, where h and k are integers with no common factor. (P = 1 when either h or k is zero; P = 3 when h = k = 1.) Only one class of virion has been found, however, with $P > 3$: Virions of the Shope papilloma (Plate XXI) and the human wart viruses have been found to be constructed according to P = 7, T = 7. For all T-values, however, if the subunit clustering is pentamer-hexamer, the following two relations hold:

S = number of structural subunits = 60 T

M = number of capsomers = 10 (T − 1) hexamers + 12 pentamers.

The various numbers of capsomers that can appear on virons of any class would be: $12, 32, 42, 72, 92, 122, 132, 162, \cdots 252 \cdots$. Many of these numbers have been reasonably well established as actually existing in the capsid structure of one or more viruses. Whether trimer clustering of subunits exists in any viral capsid, and whether the dimer clustering found in the capsid of tomato bushy stunt virus is the only example of its kind, remain to be seen.

A determination of the number of capsomers on the surface of virions of a particular virus may not be a simple matter, for at least three reasons. The virus particles may be distorted upon drying in the negative stain, thereby suffering displacement of the capsomers from their normal positions. Secondly, the capsomers on both the "top" and "bottom" surfaces of the virion will usually be projected upon the electron micrograph and may be out of register. Thirdly, the capsomers on the entire virion cannot actually be counted, one by one, since they cannot all be discerned. Capsomer *counting*, instead, comes from a simple calculation based upon observations of capsomer *arrangement*. Under the most favorable circumstance, where many particles in the electron micrograph show "one-sided" contrast and where some are appropriately oriented, it is possible to identify capsomers that are surrounded by six nearest neighbors *(six-coordinated)* and some that are surrounded by five *(five-coordinated)*. The latter will be at the vertices of the icosahedral array. If the orientation of some of the virions is such that two or more five-coordinated capsomers can be found it is usually possible to detect the number and arrangement of the six-coordinated ones lying between any two five-coordinated ones. This information will allow the T-number to be calculated. In the case of virions in the P = 1 class, the numerology is simple. If the number of intervening six-coordinated capsomers is zero, then T = 1; if the number is $1, 2, 3, 4 \cdots$ the T-numbers are 4, 9, 16, 25 $\cdots$. The clearest example of the application of this kind of examination is seen in Plate XXIV, adenovirus. Some of the virions show a triangular facet. The capsomers at the vertices are five-coordinated, with four six-coordinated ones intervening. Thus, the capsid of adenovirus has a T = 25 icosahedral lattice, with a total of 252 capsomers and 1,500 structural (protein) subunits. The P = 3 class leads to more complicated capsomeric patterns, except for the primitive T = 3 case. Here, any two five-coordinated capsomers will be joined by two six-coordinated ones in a manner such as to produce a diamond pattern, with the latter capsomers at the obtuse angles. In a particularly favorable orientation (a view down a 2-fold axis) a diamond pattern on the top surface will be in register with one on the bottom surface, yielding a pattern that is quite distinctive. Such "diamonds" can be seen on some of the virions of turnip yellow mosaic virus (Plate VIII).

The classical architectural scheme for nonenveloped, isometric viruses refers only to their capsids; nothing is said about the structural arrangement taken by the nucleic acid. From several lines of evidence, notably resistance of the nucleic acid of intact virions to nucleolytic attack, the nucleic acid is universally believed to be in the interior. But there is no firm evidence as to whether it is arrayed in a fashion that accords with the symmetry of the virion capsid. Only for tobacco mosaic virus is the form taken by the RNA known: a helical path, buried within the capsid and having the same pitch as the protein portion of the helix.

Some of the more complex viruses contain their nucleocapsids within an outer envelope. The nucleocapsid may have either icosahedral symmetry (Plate XXVI, herpes simplex virus) or helical symmetry (Plate V, Sendai virus). The latter have their nucleic acid bound to protein subunits in a helical array very much like that of tobacco mosaic virus. The nucleocapsids, or cores, of the complex virus are usually not seen in negatively stained, intact virions, although such structure can be discerned in reovirus (Plate XIII). The most striking display of nucleocapsid material is found in the disrupted virions of Sendai virus.

Virus Nomenclature and Classification

Both the naming and the grouping of viruses have been notoriously controversial subjects for many years. Historically, the rational development of nomenclature and taxonomy of viruses has been hindered by the fact that investigators from a wide variety of disciplines have discovered or isolated new viruses and have had differing opinions about the importance of the various viruses and their disease characteristics. Investigators have included biologists, physicians, entomologists, veterinarians, pathologists, and even molecular biologists, among others, so it should be no surprise that the only common attribute of the popular names ascribed has been the terminal word *virus*. For example, this *Atlas* includes virus names which describe the appearance of the infected host (tomato bushy stunt virus, tobacco mosaic virus), the town or village of isolation (Sindbis virus, Sendai virus), the diseased tissue (poliomyelitis virus, vesicular stomatitis virus), the discoverer's name (Rous sarcoma virus), acronyms (reovirus), and even coded symbols from laboratory notebooks (bacteriophage T4 and ØX174). However, since little confusion seems to have come from the use of the popular names, they have been used in this *Atlas,* rather than some Latin binomials or other system of nomenclature that has been proposed. To paraphrase Gertrude Stein, to an electron microscopist "a virus is a virus is a virus."

The customary natural grouping of the viruses by early workers was rather operational and provincial. Those who worked with plants were concerned only with the classification of plant viruses and plant virus diseases; similarly for those working with animal, bacterial, and insect viruses. Even much later, those international commissions and provisional committees formed to make recommendations for codes and classifications have been restricted to consideration of general groups of the virus hosts. For example, in 1966 the Plant Virus Subcommittee of the International Committee on Nomenclature of Viruses was established to make nomenclatural recommendations on viruses infecting plants. In 1971 they reported on sixteen groups of plant viruses. Some members of the Subcommittee, however, did not share the views of the others, and the suggestions have continued to be unofficial and must endure the test of time. It is not clear that the viruses themselves recognize and adhere to some of the proposed classifications. For example, bacteriophage seem not to recognize the taxonomic boundaries in microbiology, and some so-called plant and animal viruses multiply in insect hosts as well as in their recognized plant or animal hosts. *In vitro* systems of subcellular compositions have been devised which cross taxonomic boundaries for the growth of some bacteriophage components in animal cell systems and for the growth of some animal virus nucleic acid in purified enzyme systems from *E. coli.*

Even though continuation, for the present, of the use of popular names of viruses seems justified, it is difficult to arrive at a sequence for the presentation of the pictures of viruses in this *Atlas* without entering into "the religious war of taxonomy." A collection of electron micrographs of viruses portrays only what one sees, and so its arrangement is logically governed by the properties of structure, the molecular biology, and the geometry of the capsids of the virions. Since viruses can be distinguished from the rest of the biological world because they contain either RNA or DNA, but not both, a grand subdivision based on the chemical nature of their genetic material is universally accepted. Lwoff, Horne, and Tournier proposed a system of virus classification (the LHT system) in which a division on the basis of the kind of nucleic acid was the first of four discriminating characteristics or "essential integrants." The remaining three relate to what is seen in a high-resolution electron micrograph of a virion. The four characteristics are:

1. The chemical nature of the genetic material, either **DNA or RNA,** determining the subphyla.
2. The symmetry of the nucleocapsid of the virion: helical, cubic, or binal, determining the classes.
3. The covering of the nucleocapsid, either naked or enveloped, determining the orders.
4. The size of the nucleocapsid, either the diameter of the helix or the number of capsomers in the cubic system, determining the families.

The way these criteria have been utilized in the *Atlas* is shown in the accompanying chart that lists the popular names of typical family members to be found in the *Atlas.* Attention should be called to some special features of organization: (1) the helical arrangement of the nucleocapsid of the bullet-shaped vesicular stomatitis virus is very different from that of the influenza and Sendai viruses which are also helical RNA viruses with envelopes; (2) Rous sarcoma virus does not yet have its nucleocapsid structure established; and (3) the binal DNA viruses (i.e. the phage with isometric heads and helical tails) have been separated according to whether they are virulent or temperate. Although the chart shows subdivision of orders into families only on the basis of relative size, the LHT system specified the exact number of capsomers and triangulation number for viruses with cubic symmetry, and the diameter for viruses with helical symmetry. Details about these structural characteristics can be found in the discussion which accompanies each Plate. Lwoff and Tournier have further suggested that the families may be subdivided into many genera according to additional characters such as the number of strands of nucleic acid and its circularity, base composition and nucleotide sequence, the molecular weight of the structural proteins, immunochemistry of the capsomers, enzymes determined by the genetic material, site of synthesis of viral materials, virus-cell interactions, host specificity, virulence and symptomology, to mention a few. These fine distinctions are clearly beyond the scope of the organization plan of the *Atlas*. Many of these properties are mentioned in the discussion accompanying each Plate.

Suggestions have been made that a cryptogram should follow the vernacular name of a virus in order to describe in shorthand fashion a few salient facts about the virus. Such a cryptogram would contain four pairs of symbols with the following meanings: the first pair of symbols to state the type of nucleic acid and its strandedness; the second pair to give the molecular weight of the nucleic acid and its percentage content in the virion in the particles; the third pair to specify the outline of the shape of the entire particle and the outline of its nucleocapsid; and the fourth pair to name the kinds of hosts and kinds of vectors. Since the information added by a cryptogram depends upon the reader's memory of the meaning of the symbols, cryptograms have not been included in the *Atlas*.

CRITERIA FOR CLASSIFICATION OF VIRUSES

Nucleic acid	Symmetry	Presence of envelope	Size	Members included in Atlas
RNA	Helical	no	small	Potato Virus X
			medium	Tobacco Mosaic Virus
			large	Tobacco Rattle Virus
		yes	medium	Influenza Virus, Sendai Virus, Vesicular Stomatitis
	Cubic	no	small	Phage MS2, Turnip Yellow Mosaic Virus, Satellite Tobacco Necrosis Virus, Brome Mosaic Virus
			medium	Poliovirus, Tomato Bushy Stunt Virus
			large	Reovirus, Wound Tumor Virus, Cytoplasmic Polyhedrosis Virus
		yes	medium	Rous Sarcoma Virus, Sindbis Virus
DNA	Helical	no	small	fd Phage
		yes	large	Vaccinia Virus
	Cubic	no	small	Phage ΦX174
			medium	Papilloma Virus, Simian Virus 40, Cauliflower Mosaic Virus
			large	Adenovirus
			huge	Tipula Iridescent Virus
		yes	large	Herpes Virus
	Cubic, tailed (binal)	virulent		Phage T4, Phage T5, Phage T7
		temperate		Phage Lambda, Phage P2

SELECTED BIBLIOGRAPHY
OF VIRUS STRUCTURE

Anon: Editorial note. *Neth J Plant Pathol, 76:* 227, 1970.

Caspar, D. L. D., Dulbecco, R., Klug, A., Lwoff, A., Stoker, M. G. P., Tournier, P., and Wildy, P.: Proposals. *Cold Spring Harbor Symp Quant Biol, 27:* 49, 1962.

Caspar, D. L. D., and Klug, A.: Physical principles in the construction of regular viruses. *Cold Spring Harbor Symp Quant Biol, 27:* 1, 1962.

Crane, H. R.: Principles and problems of biological growth. *Sci Monthly, 70:* 376, 1950.

Crick, F. H. C., and Watson, J. D.: Structure of small viruses. *Nature (Lond), 177:* 473, 1956.

Eiserling, F. A., and Dickson, R. C.: Assembly of viruses. *Annu Rev Biochem, 41:* 467, 1972.

Harrison, B. D., Finch, J. T., Gibbs, A. J., Hollings, M., Shepherd, R. J., Valenta, V., and Wetter, C.: Sixteen groups of plant viruses. *Virology, 45:* 356, 1971.

Horne, R. W., and Wildy, P.: Symmetry in virus architecture. *Virology, 15:* 348, 1961.

Kushner, D. J.: Self-assembly of biological structures. *Bacteriol Rev, 33:* 302, 1969.

Lwoff, A., and Tournier, P.: The classification of viruses. *Annu Rev Microbiol, 20:* 45, 1966.

ACKNOWLEDGMENTS

Many persons have contributed to the development of this volume. First to be thanked are those who gave us samples of viruses to be photographed in the electron microscope. Colleagues in the Virus Laboratory who furnished specimens:

R. Calendar—Plates XXVII, XXIX, XXXI
P. H. Duesberg—Plate XVI
H. Echols—Plate XXX
H. Fraenkel—Conrat—Plate IX
C. A. Knight—Plates I, II, IV, VIII, XII, XXI
L. J. Lewandowski—Plates XIII, XIV
B. L. Traynor—Plate XV

Other persons generously sent virus specimens by mail:

I. J. Bendet—Plate XVIII
R. W. Darlington—Plate XXVI
E. Fowlks—Plate X, Figure 11
K. A. Hartman—Plate VII, Figure 8
D. W. Kingsbury—Plate V
R. M. Lister—Plate III
D. J. McCorquodale—Plate XXVIII
E. R. Pfefferkorn—Plate XVII
R. W. Schlesinger—Plate XXIV
R. J. Shepherd—Plate XXIII
R. L. Sinsheimer—Plate XX
D. F. Summers—Plate VI
A. Weissbach—Plate XIX

We wish to express our gratitude to them.

Able technical assistance in the laboratory was provided by Joseph Toby and Toni Klassen. Invaluable secretarial assistance was given by Loretta Hurren whose typing of the manuscript showed her unexcelled passion for accuracy.

While this *Atlas* was being assembled, one of us (RCW) was supported in part in his research efforts by Public Health Service Research Grant CA 02245 from the National Cancer Institute, and during an extensive period in 1970 the other (HWF) was supported by a National Institutes of Health Fellowship (CA 42637) from the National Cancer Institute.

R.C.W.
H.W.F.

CONTENTS

AN ELECTRON
MICROGRAPHIC ATLAS
OF VIRUSES

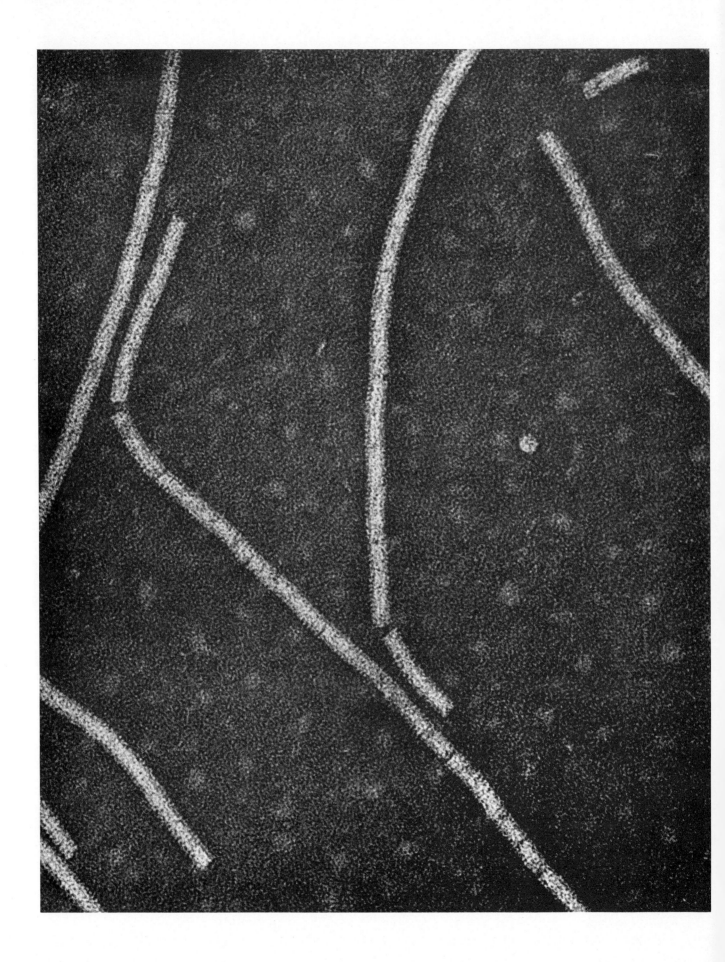

PLATE I POTATO VIRUS X x400,000

RNA, single-stranded, 5 percent

Flexuous rod, helical, 12 nm × *ca.* 500 nm

Diseases of potato plants caused by potato virus X (PVX) are widely spread throughout the world. While the symptoms produced are not generally severe, a common attribute of most plant-virus diseases, the effect of infection by the virus is an appreciable reduction in yield and quality of the crop. It has been estimated that infection by the virus causes a 10 percent diminution of crop yield, averaged over the earth, a serious loss in those regions where the potato is the primary source of nutrition.

Potato plants infected with PVX are now known to be frequently co-infected with a relatively unrelated virus, called potato virus Y (PVY). As early as 1931, some years before viruses were known to be particles and hence purifiable by physical and chemical means, K. M. Smith pointed out the possibility that simultaneous infections with PVX and PVY might be common and devised a method for obtaining pure infections by either virus. This was done by serial inoculations of sap, either by mechanical means or insect transmission, to a variety of solanaceous plants. He discovered that one of the two viruses (which he called potato virus Y) could be insect-transmitted, while the other could not. This provided for the production of PVY infections free of PVX. He then found a plant species that was resistant to PVY but susceptible to mechanical inoculation of sap containing both PVX and PVY. He correctly reasoned that sap from those plants contained no PVY and, very likely, contained only PVX. This work by Smith introduced the procedure, now in common use, by which bacterial cells are found to serve as *indicator strains* for biological isolation of particular strains of bacteriophage.

Potato virus X is commonly grown on tomato or tobacco plants for laboratory purposes. Its yield may be as high as 0.7 gm of virus per liter of infectious juice, allowing ready purification in rather large quantities. The purified virus particles have been examined by x-ray diffraction of oriented gels and by electron microscopy. The virion has the form of an elongated, flexuous rod, about 500 nm long and 11.5 nm in diameter. The early x-ray work showed it to have a periodicity of structure along its length, a result later confirmed by high-resolution electron microscopy. Electron micrographs show an axial periodicity of 3.3 to 3.4 nm, and optical diffractograms of the best pictures indicate that the form of the virus nucleocapsid is a helix. What appear to be short segments of the virion are occasionally seen (Plate I). Whether or not the virion contains a central hole, such as there is in TMV (Plate II) has been debatable, but it has been reported that superposition photography shows a central hole surrounded by 10 subunits.

Potato virus X contains only protein and RNA, in a 20 to 1 ratio. It is disassembled rather readily, with phenol commonly used as the reagent when the RNA is wanted and guanidine-HCl for preservation of the protein in solution. Only recently has the molecular weight of the protein subunit been convincingly established. It was earlier thought to be about 52,000 daltons, from physicochemical measurements, but recent amino acid analyses have set its value at 22,300 daltons (210 amino acid residues). Although the RNA and protein of PVX are not too difficult to obtain in undenatured form, it is only recently that this virus has been successfully reconstituted *in vitro* to yield infectious particles.

An intriguing anomaly has recently been found in the antigenic relationship of the intact virion of PVX to its protein subunits. As with many other viruses, PVX protein subunits may be obtained by chemical degradation of the purified virion or by extraction of presumably

3

unassembled structural units from the infected cell. The former protein is usually found to have an antigenicity that is quite distinct from that of the intact virion; this distinction holds for PVX. In most virus infections (and, heretofore, in all plant virus infections) the cellular virus-specific protein is antigenically similar, if not identical, to the virion. In PVX infections, however, this protein differs markedly in its antigenic properties from those of the virion and resembles that of the protein obtained by virion degradation. This finding points up the possibility that serological tests for the existence of unassembled viral protein within cells, if these tests use antigenic similarity with the intact virion as the criterion, may occasionally be falsely negative.

Selected Bibliography

Bawden, F. C., and Pirie, N. W.: Liquid crystalline preparations of potato virus X. *Br J Exp Pathol, 19:* 66, 1938.

Matthews, R. E. F.: *Plant Virology.* New York and London, Acad Pr, 1970, pp. 108–109.

Miki, T., and Knight, C. A.: The protein subunit of potato virus X. *Virology, 36:* 168, 1968.

Shalla, T. A., and Shepard, J. F.: A virus induced soluble antigen associated with potato virus-X infection. *Virology, 42:* 1130, 1970.

Smith, K. M.: On the composite nature of certain potato virus diseases of the mosaic group as revealed by the use of plant indicators and selective methods of transmission. *Proc R Soc Lond, B109:* 251, 1931.

Varma, A., Gibbs, A. J., Woods, R. D., and Finch, J. T.: Some observations on the structure of the filamentous particles of several plant viruses. *J Gen Virol, 2:* 107, 1968.

PLATE II

TOBACCO MOSAIC VIRUS

x535,000

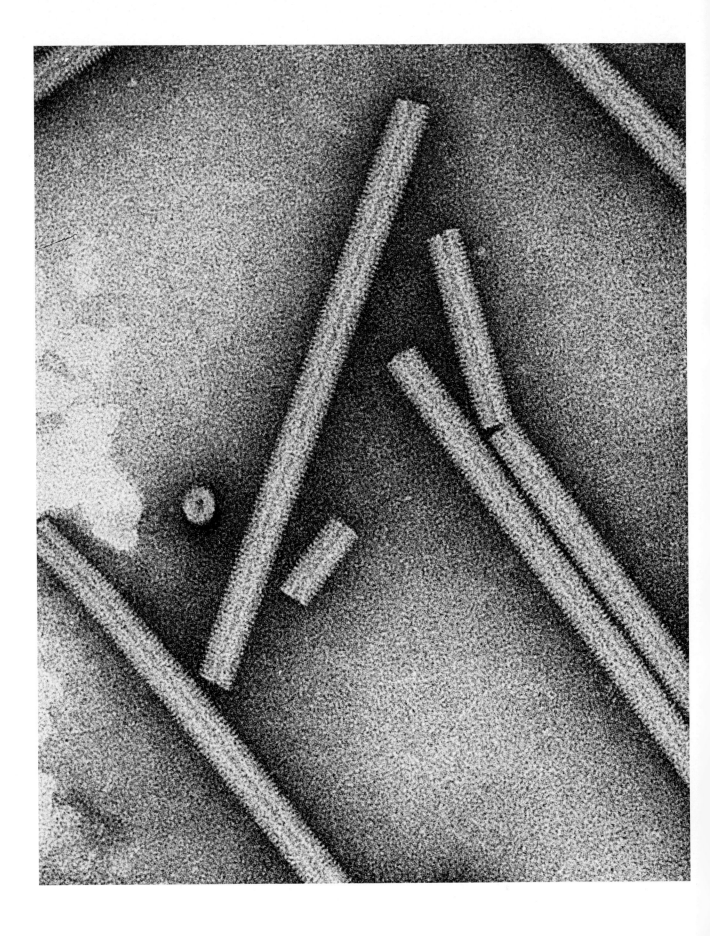

PLATE II   TOBACCO MOSAIC VIRUS   x535,000

RNA, single-stranded, 5 percent

Rigid rod, helical, 18 nm × 300 nm

Viruses were initially recognized only as infectious agents having the property of passage through filters too fine to pass any known microbial body. But in 1935 W. M. Stanley announced that he had purified the agent of tobacco mosaic disease, had crystallized it by methods used in the crystallization of proteins, and had found it to be a protein. Shortly thereafter ribonucleic acid was found in tobacco mosaic virus (TMV), and its identity as a rod-shaped particle was established by direct observation in the electron microscope and by inference from sedimentation analysis and from studies of streaming birefringence. During the 1950's greatly increased knowledge of the structure of the virions of TMV was obtained. X-ray analysis showed them to have a helical structure, with a pitch of 2.3 nm, each turn of the helix containing $16\frac{1}{3}$ structural subunits. These subunits were later identified with a protein molecule having a weight of 17,530 daltons and containing 158 amino acid residues. Since there are 131 turns of the helix in one TMV particle, the number of protein molecules is 2,140, and the total weight of protein is 3.75×10^7 daltons. The total weight of the virus, including its 5 percent RNA, is very close to 4.0×10^7 daltons. The RNA is also arrayed in helical form, probably with three nucleotides bound to each protein subunit, but under appropriate conditions of partial degradation it can be seen as a slender fiber extending from the virion (Fig. 3).

The common strain of TMV produces relatively mild mottling and discoloration on the leaves of plants undergoing systemic infection. Electron micrographs of sections of leaf tissue show virus particles in great abundance, lined up in palisade array. Three-dimensional crystals are found, particularly in leaf hairs, consisting of closely aligned virus particles (Fig. 4). These are apparently assembled in the cytoplasm, al-

Figure 3. Electron micrograph of particles of tobacco mosaic virus which have been partially degraded to expose their RNA. Shadowed with uranium. (White disc is an unshadowed sphere of polystyrene latex.) ×60,000.

though some involvement with the nucleus has been suggested.

Both the protein and the single-stranded RNA of TMV can be isolated in undegraded form. The former exists as a monomer only under fairly extreme conditions of low concen-

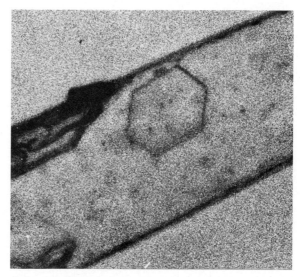

Figure 4. Light micrograph of a crystal of tobacco mosaic virus within a leaf hair.

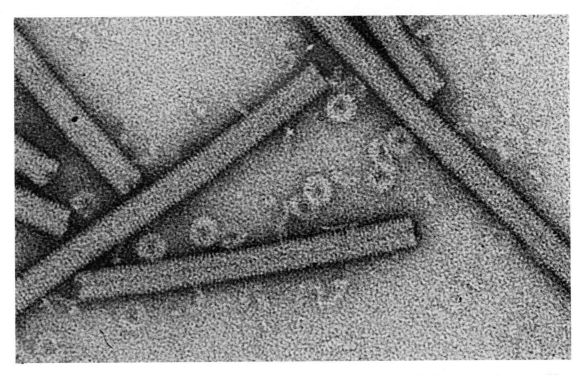

Figure 5. Portions of helical rods formed by polymerization of the protein of tobacco mosaic virus. Note the similarity in appearance of these rods with those of the native virus (Plate II). ×440,000.

tration, low ionic strength, low temperature, and high pH (above 10.5), but under near-physiological conditions it exists almost entirely as an equilibrium mixture of trimer (4S) and a two-ring disc of 34 monomers (20S). Long helical rods are formed if a TMV protein solution, at room temperature and in about 0.01 M salt, is dropped to pH 6.5 or lower. Polymerization of the protein from monomer to helical rods (Fig. 5) is reversible, with low temperature, low ionic strength, and high pH favoring depolymerization. Calorimetric experiments show that polymerization of the protein is endothermic and that bound water is released, properties indicating that hydrophobic bonds are formed upon polymerization.

It was first found in 1955 that the purified protein and RNA of TMV can be reconstituted to form rods morphologically indistinguishable from intact TMV and having infectivity potential not greatly reduced from that of the native virus. There followed shortly the demonstration that the RNA, alone, is infectious. For reasons not wholly understood, but probably related to its mechanical fragility and susceptibility to RNAse action, the RNA is only frac-

tionally as infectious as its equivalent amount when covered by protein coat, as it is in the native or reconstituted virus.

Recent work has partially elucidated the mechanism of TMV reconstitution. In order for the reaction to be initiated the protein-RNA mixture must contain the two-ring discs. The first step in the reaction is the attachment of 50 or so nucleotides adjacent to the 5'-hydroxyl end of the RNA to the protein monomers that make up one face of the disc; if the native 5'-hydroxyl end is removed by action of spleen phosphodiesterase reconstitution does not start. The attachment of the RNA to the protein subunits on one planar surface of the two-ring disc presumably induces a conformational change of the latter to form a "lock-washer," thus the start of a helix. Following initiation of the assembly the next process, elongation, takes place. Since it will proceed under conditions in which no discs exist, it evidently involves the trimeric or monomeric form of the protein. As these units become sequentially attached to the RNA a helix is formed, with the RNA intercalated between adjacent turns of the helical structure. The rod grows in length

Plate II—Tobacco Mosaic Virus 9

until all the RNA chain is incorporated within it. High-resolution electron micrographs of native TMV and reconstituted TMV appear identical.

Selected Bibliography

Butler, P. J. G., and Klug, A.: Assembly of the particle of tobacco mosaic virus from RNA and disks of protein. *Nature [New Biol]*, *229:* 47, 1971.

Durham, A. C. H., Finch, J. T., and Klug, A.: States of aggregation of tobacco mosaic virus protein. *Nature [New Biol]*, *229:* 37, 1971.

Fraenkel-Conrat, H., and Williams, R. C.: Reconstitution of active tobacco mosaic virus from its inactive protein and nucleic acid components. *Proc Natl Acad Sci USA, 41:* 690, 1955.

Franklin, R. E., and Holmes, K. C.: The helical arrangement of the protein sub-units in tobacco mosaic virus. *Biochim Biophys Acta, 21:* 405, 1956.

Lauffer, M. A., and Stevens, C. L.: Structure of the tobacco mosaic virus particle; polymerization of tobacco mosaic virus protein. *Adv Virus Res, 13:* 1, 1968.

Richards, K. E., and Williams, R. C.: Assembly of tobacco mosaic virus *in vitro:* Effect of state of polymerization of the protein component. *Proc Natl Acad Sci USA, 69:* 1121, 1972.

Stanley, W. M.: Isolation of a crystalline protein possessing the properties of tobacco-mosaic virus. *Science, 81:* 644, 1935.

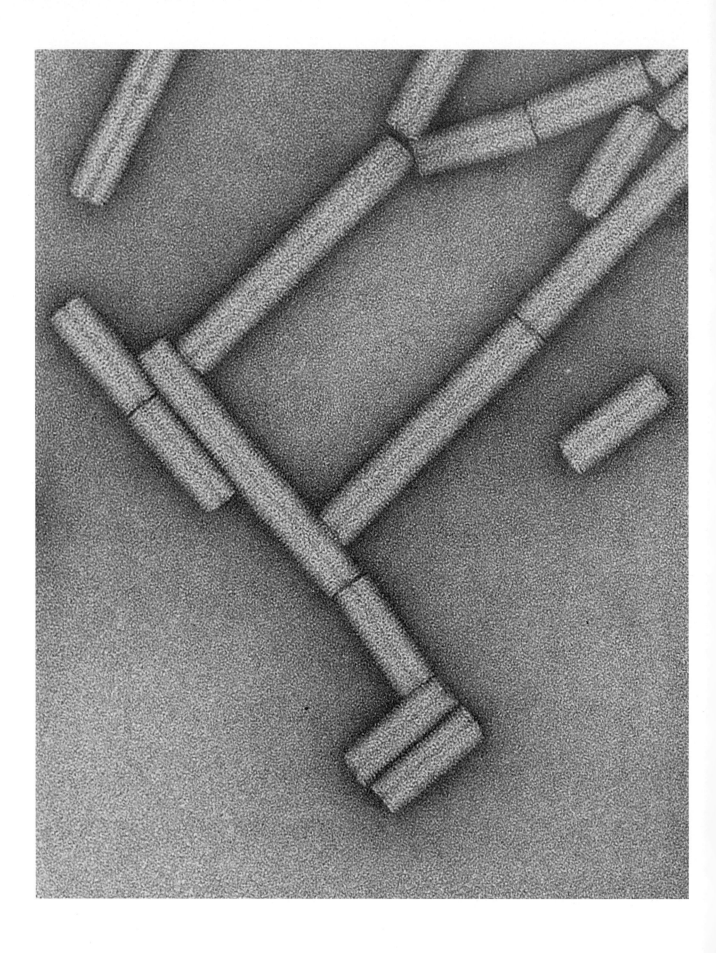

PLATE III   TOBACCO RATTLE VIRUS   x 445,000

RNA, single-stranded, 5 percent

Rigid rod, helical, 25 nm × 180 nm

ATTENTION was first brought to the interesting properties of tobacco rattle virus (TRV) in 1955 when Paul and Bode showed that purified preparations of the virus consisted of particles of two distinctive lengths, one not a simple multiple of the other. The virions, whether of the longer or shorter type, are generally similar in structure to potato virus X (Plate I) and tobacco mosaic virus (Plate II) : helical rods of nucleoprotein with an RNA content of about 5 percent. Detailed work with the aid of x-ray analysis and electron microscopy has provided a generally agreed upon picture of the architectural details of the TRV virions. Preparations from a given isolate of the Oregon strain (Plate III) contain particles of two greatly differing lengths, with the longer falling in the vicinity of 180 nm while the shorter is usually less than half this length. Diameters of the individual rods are much more uniform; most investigators have agreed upon a value of 25.0 to 25.5 nm. The pitch of the TRV helix, determined both from electron microscopy and x-ray analysis, is well established at close to 2.5 nm. Like tobacco mosaic virus, the helix has a nonintegral number of structural subunits per turn; TMV has 49 subunits in three turns, while TRV probably has 76 subunits in the same number of turns. Since the TRV protein subunit is only slightly larger than that of TMV (*ca.* 20,000 *vs.* 17,500 daltons) it is seen that its virion is essentially a fatter version of TMV: same pitch, but more subunits per turn, yielding a larger diameter helix.

When an unfractionated preparation of an isolate of TRV is inoculated to an appropriate host, local lesions are produced. Separate lesions contain a sample of the inoculated material: rods of two differing lengths. But if the starting material is fractionated and only the long rods are inoculated to plants, local lesions are produced but no virus rods are recoverable from them. There is, however, relatively unstable infectious material in the lesions, extractable with phenol. Inoculation with the shorter rods of the starting material produces no observable symptoms. The RNA in both the longer and shorter rods is extractable with phenol; inoculation with this mixed material produces the same pattern of results as does inoculation with the intact rods. Both the long and short rods may be reconstituted (protein and RNA fractions reassembled *in vitro*) by methods similar to those used for tobacco mosaic virus.

In 1965 R. M. Lister suggested that the infectivity studies with TRV could be explained if the long rods and the short ones had distinctive functions in virus-multiplication events. He proposed that the genome of the long rods could not code for the production of viral protein but did code for an RNA polymerase involved in the replication of both the long-rod and the short-rod RNA. On the other hand, the genome of the short rods carried the code message for production of viral protein but contained no message for a polymerase. Such explanation is in accord with the phenomena: long rods alone produce only infectious RNA in the local lesions; short rods alone produce no viral RNA and hence no lesions; the two rod types together contain the coding necessary for production of both infectious RNA and the viral coat protein—a classic example of symbiosis, at the level of viruses. All later work has tended to support the viability of Lister's proposal.

Tobacco rattle virus has recently been reconstituted from its protein and nucleic acid components. As with TMV (Plate II), the initiation of reconstitution requires the presence of two-ring discs, and elongation can proceed in the absence of disc forms.

11

Selected Bibliography

Frost, R. R., Harrison, B. D., and Woods, R. D.: Apparent symbiotic interaction between particles of tobacco rattle virus. *J Gen Virol, 1:* 57, 1967.

Lister, R. M.: Possible relationships of virus-specific products of tobacco rattle virus infections. *Virology, 28:* 350, 1966.

Matthews, R. E. F.: *Plant Virology.* New York and London, Acad Pr, 1970, pp. 227–251.

Miki, T., and Okada, Y.: Comparative studies on some strains of tobacco rattle virus. *Virology, 42:* 993, 1970.

Offord, R. E.: Electron microscopic observations on the substructure of tobacco rattle virus. *J Mol Biol, 17:* 370, 1966.

Paul, H. L., and Bode, O.: Elektronenmikroskopische untersuchungen über kartoffelviren. II. Vermessung der teilchen von drei stämmen des rattle-virus. *Phytopathol Z, 24:* 341, 1955.

Tollin, P., and Wilson, H. R.: Some observations on the structure of the Campinas strain of tobacco rattle virus. *J Gen Virol, 13:* 433, 1971.

PLATE IV

INFLUENZA VIRUS

x 310,000

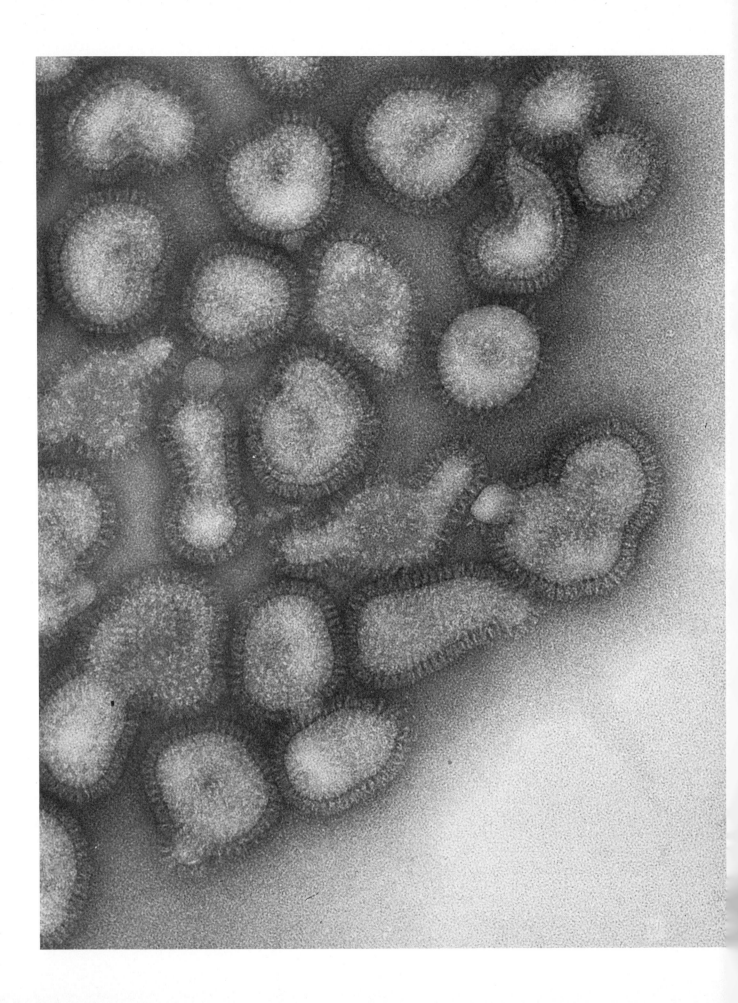

PLATE IV INFLUENZA VIRUS x 310,000

RNA, single-stranded, 1 percent

Pleomorphic, enveloped and fringed, *ca.* 100 nm; helical nucleocapsid, 9 nm diameter

THE INFLUENZA VIRUS is the historical type example of what has come to be called myxoviruses. These viruses are distinguished by certain common properties: (1) They are infectious to mammals, (2) they agglutinate red blood cells and enzymatically attack their mucin component by destruction of neuraminic acid, and (3) the virions are roughly spherical (in the diameter range 100 to 200 nm), with an internal, helical capsid of ribonucleoprotein and an outer, spiked envelope containing hemagglutinin and neuraminidase as well as carbohydrate and lipid.

Early work by Burnet showed that influenza virus infections had a high frequency of genetic recombination and multiplicity rescue of ultraviolet-induced inactivation; both effects pointed to the likelihood that the influenza genome was multiple. Another phenomenon, named after its discoverer, von Magnus, was the production of relatively noninfectious material (as measured by infectivity/hemagglutinin ratio) when virus was serially passaged at high multiplicity in the experimental host, the allantoic fluid of the chick embryo.

Recent observations on the nucleocapsid material, and on its RNA component, have served to elucidate both the phenomenon of genetic recombination and of the occurrence of noninfectious influenza virions (the von Magnus phenomenon). When virions of influenza are exposed to a lipid solvent, such as ether, they are disrupted into a nucleocapsid component and one containing fragments of the envelope. The former component, helical structures of variable length and 9 nm diameter, may be purified and its RNA component extracted with phenol. Gradient centrifugation shows that the nucleocapsid material is analytically separable into at least three size categories; the RNA exists in at least five separable components, as shown by centrifugation and

gel electrophoresis. It appears, then, that the influenza virus genome is multiple, both as naked RNA and as it exists in the nucleocapsid. These findings, of course, explain in qualitative terms the phenomena of genetic recombination and multiplicity reactivation. Analysis of the RNA in preparations of low infectivity/hemagglutinin ratio (rich in von Magnus virus) shows a relative deficiency of the faster-sedimenting material. Evidently, then, an inoculation at high multiplicity results in the formation of virions containing an incomplete quota of RNA, for reasons unknown. On the next round of high-multiplicity, serial passage these virions replicate preferentially over the normal ones, thus increasing the relative number of von Magnus particles. These particles appear to have normal agglutinating activity, but are not infectious; i.e. they do not induce a cell pathology that can be scored as a lesion when tested on the chorioallantoic membrane.

The existence of hemagglutinating and neuraminidase activity on the outer envelope of influenza virus particles is well established. It is thought that these phenomena relate to the attachment and release of virions in the natural process of host-cell inoculation. The existence of *spikes* on the surface of the virions (Plate IV) is also well documented. Treatments which remove the visible spikes abolish infectivity and both hemagglutinating and neuraminidase activity. What is not firmly established is the morphology of the enzymes responsible for these activities and the form of their array on the virion surface. The entire envelope contains polypeptides, glycopolypeptides, and lipids. The last is added to the virion from the host cell as *budding* from the cell membrane occurs, but the former two are virus-specified. The whole virion contains at least seven proteins, in the molecular weight range of 25,000 to 80,000 daltons. Of these, four are glycoproteins and three of these are missing from the virion when the spike material is chemically removed. One nonglycoprotein is believed to be the protein component of the nucleocapsid; the other two nonglycoproteins and the remaining protein may be part of the structure of the envelope that is not in the form of spikes but confers structural integrity to the spikeless membrane.

Hemagglutinin and neuraminidase from influenza virions have been separately purified. The former appears in the electron microscope as a rod about 14 nm long and 4 nm in diameter when in a preparation that contains sodium dodecyl sulphate, but when this reagent is removed the material aggregates into rosettes. There is not universal agreement as to the morphology of the neuraminidase, but Laver and Valentine found it to appear as a short cylinder about 8.5 nm long to which is centrally attached, at right angles, a thin fiber with a small knob at its distal end. From the electron microscopic evidence it would be concluded that both the hemagglutinin and neuraminidase would have a molecular weight of about 150,000 daltons, a figure about three times greater than is found by gel electrophoresis for any influenza viral protein. Electron micrographs of influenza virions frequently show small, triangular-shaped objects on the virion surfaces. Laver and Valentine believe these to be the hemagglutinin structures seen end-on. Whatever may be the detailed form of the two components making up the spikes it seems likely that they are arrayed in intermixed fashion on the envelope exterior.

Influenza virus replication, in distinction from that of the parainfluenza viruses, has an intranuclear phase. Shortly after inoculation a fluorescent antibody against the nucleocapsid shows a strong reaction in the nuclear region of the cell, indicating that early synthesis of the protein component takes place there. It is possible that the entire nucleocapsid is formed within the nucleus. Later in the infection the nucleocapsid cores migrate to the cell membrane. The hemagglutinin and neuraminidase also migrate to the membrane, where they replace the cell membrane in discrete patches. At a later stage the cores protrude through the membrane; in the ensuing budding they are encapsulated in an envelope which contains cellular lipid and the virus-specific hemagglutinin and neuraminidase. During RNA synthesis, as with other single-stranded RNA viruses, double-stranded RNA is found in the cytoplasm. Six different species are found, indicating that each segment of the viral genome replicates independently of the others.

Selected Bibliography

Burnet, F. M.: Structure of influenza virus. *Science,* 123: 1101, 1956.

Burnet, F. M., and Lind, P. E.: A genetic approach to variation in influenza viruses. 4. Recombination of characters between the influenza virus A strain NWS and strains of different serological subtypes. *J Gen Microbiol, 5:* 67, 1951.

Compans, R. W., Klenk, H.-D., Caliguiri, L. A., and Choppin, P. W.: Influenza virus proteins. 1. Analysis of polypeptides of the virion and identification of spike glycoproteins. *Virology, 42:* 880, 1970.

Laver, W. G., and Valentine, R. C.: Morphology of the isolated hemagglutinin and neuraminidase subunits of influenza virus. *Virology, 38:* 105, 1969.

Robinson, W. S., and Duesberg, P. H.: The myxoviruses. In Fraenkel-Conrat, H. (Ed.): *Molecular Basis of Virology.* New York, Reinhold, 1968, pp. 255–305.

von Magnus, P.: Incomplete forms of influenza virus. *Adv Virus Res, II:* 59, 1954.

PLATE V

SENDAI VIRUS

x 300,000

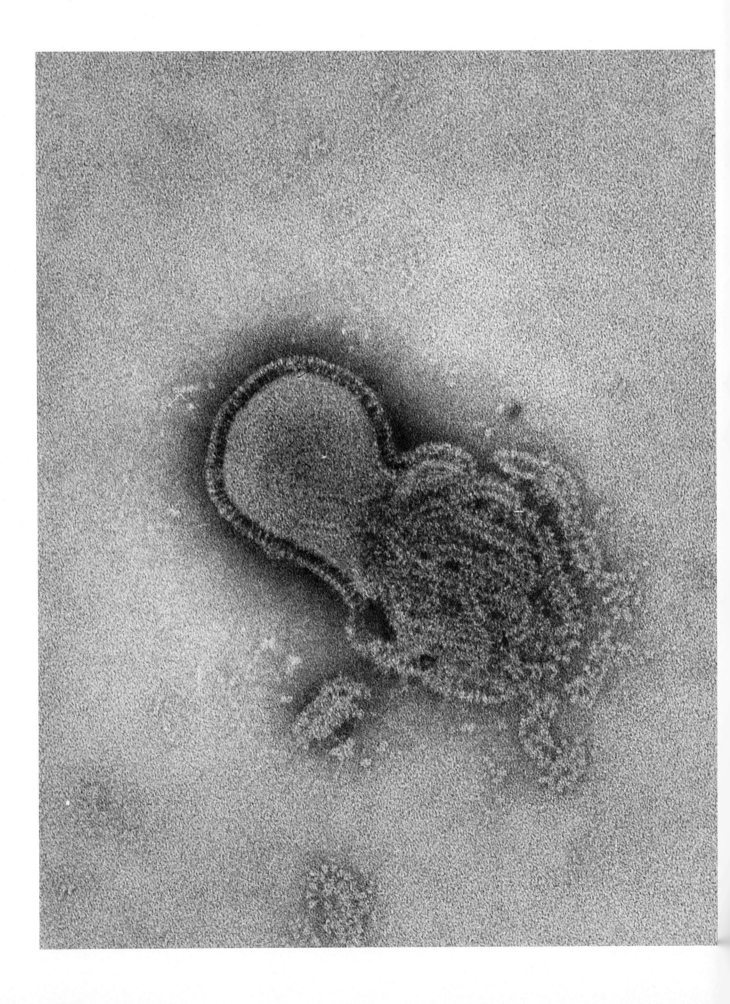

PLATE V   SENDAI VIRUS   x 300,000

RNA, single-stranded, about 1 percent

Isometric, enveloped and fringed, *ca.* 100–200 nm; helical nucleocapsid 17 nm diameter

SENDAI VIRUS, also known as HVJ (hemagglutinating virus of Japan), is a large, pleomorphic, enveloped virus whose structure, both internal and external, has close similarities to other viruses of the paramyxo group. It is classified explicitly as parainfluenza virus I. Its central region, or core, contains its nucleocapsid in the form of long, rigid rods of helical form composed of protein and about 4 percent single-stranded RNA. Around this core, in the intact virion, is an envelope composed of protein, glycoprotein, and glycolipids; it is morphologically distinctive by possessing an array of *spikes,* or protuberances. Two recognizable functions are associated with the envelope: hemagglutinating activity and neuraminidase activity. Virions prepared for electron microscopy by negative staining are most frequently seen disrupted (Plate V), disclosing the morphological distinctions between their inner and outer portions.

When the spikes are removed from the Sendai envelope (as assessed by electron microscopy) by the action of a protease the virions lose both their ability to clump red blood cells and to hydrolyze the neuraminic acid on red cell membranes. They also lose much of their infectivity, presumably because they are no longer able to attach to cells. The spikes themselves, of two types, are known to be glycoproteins, with molecular weights of about 75,000 daltons (hemagglutinin) and 50,000 daltons (neuraminidase). So far, the electron microscope has not distinguished the two functionally different kinds of spikes. It seems most probable that the envelope of Sendai virus derives in greatest part from the cellular membrane, both from virus-specified and host-cell-specified components. Electron microscopy of sections shows that the whole virion is assembled only at the cell membrane, at a time after the preformed nucleocapsids have migrated from the perinuclear region to certain specific places on the membrane. These regions have evidently been altered to have virus-specific composition in their polypeptides, although the carbohydrate portion of the viral glycopeptides and the lipid components of the virion envelope (about 20%) may be host-cell-specific. It is only when the nucleocapsids are close to the cell membrane that they take on the hemagglutinin and neuraminidase activity. The coating of the nucleocapsid by the full virion envelope is apparently completed when it buds from the cell surface. It is possible for more than one nucleocapsid to become encapsulated in the same envelope, since very large virions are found that appear to have multiple nucleocapsids.

Observations by electron microscopy indicate that the nucleocapsid of a Sendai virion is a nucleoprotein helix about 1 μm in length. What fraction of the virion mass is nucleocapsid is not known, but since the intact virion has about 1 percent RNA content, and the nucleocapsid has 4 percent, it is concluded that 25 percent of the virion mass is nucleocapsid. The nucleocapsid helix has overall similarity to the virion of tobacco mosaic virus (Plate II), but aside from its greater length it differs structurally in some detail (Fig. 6). Its RNA content is only 4 percent, the pitch of the helix is 5 nm instead of 2.6 nm, while its protein monomer has a molecular weight of about 60,000 (rather than 17,500) daltons. The single-stranded RNA within the nucleocapsid is resistant to ribonuclease digestion, presumably owing to its protected position within the helix. As mentioned above, the nucleocapsids in an infected cell arrange themselves along the cell membrane, awaiting encapsulation, but in some types of infections with Sendai virus the efficiency of encapsulation is evidently low, resulting in vast accumulation of nucleocapsid material within the cytoplasm.

19

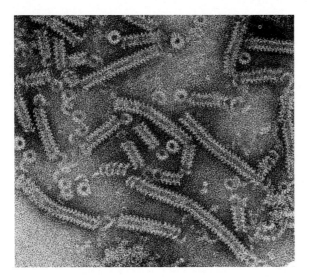

Figure 6. Fragments of nucleocapsid released from Sendai virus. The helical structure is notably more open than that of tobacco mosaic virus (Plate II), and the central channel is wider. ×180,000.

In common with other viruses of the paramyxo group the virions of Sendai virus, when mixed with cells growing in culture, cause the formation of syncytia: cells which have fused to form a large cell with multiple nuclei. Successful infection by the virus is apparently not necessary for this effect to be produced, since virions which have been inactivated by ultraviolet light or β-propiolactone are effective cell-fusion agents. It is not known whether cell fusion is caused by the envelope portion or the nucleocapsid portion of the virion, or whether, indeed, it is brought about by some viral component as yet unidentified.

With respect to the foregoing description, the properties of Sendai virus are very similar to those of another parainfluenza virus, Newcastle disease virus. The most notable distinction between the two viruses is their natural host range. Sendai virus has been found in pigs and in mice, while Newcastle disease virus (NDV) is widely spread as a formidable scourge of chickens and other fowl. At the laboratory level of experimentation the two viruses are found to have two primary differences, probably not unrelated. Their RNA's have practically the same nucleotide composition, but hybridization experiments show that they have little, if any, sequence homology. As messengers they must code differently for polypeptide sequences. It is therefore not surprising that the two viruses are also found to be antigenically dissimilar.

Selected Bibliography

Blair, C. D., and Robinson, W. S.: Replication of Sendai virus. II. Steps in virus assembly. *J Virol,* 5: 639, 1970.

Compans, R. W., and Choppin, P. W.: The structure and assembly of influenza and parainfluenza viruses. In Maramorosch, K., and Kurstak, E. (Eds.): *Comparative Virology,* New York, Acad Pr, 1971, pp. 407–432.

Joklik, W. K., and Zweerink, H. J.: The morphogenesis of animal viruses. *Annu Rev Genet, 5:* 297, 1971.

Mountcastle, W. E., Compans, R. W., and Choppin, P. W.: Proteins and glycoproteins of paramyxoviruses: a comparison of simian virus 5, Newcastle disease virus, and Sendai virus. *J Virol, 7:* 47, 1971.

Okada, Y.: The fusion of Ehrlich's tumor cells caused by H.V.J. virus *in vitro. Biken J, 1:* 103, 1958.

Poste, G.: Virus-induced polykaryocytosis and the mechanism of cell fusion. *Adv Virus Res, 16:* 303, 1970.

PLATE VI

VESICULAR STOMATITIS VIRUS

x 320,000

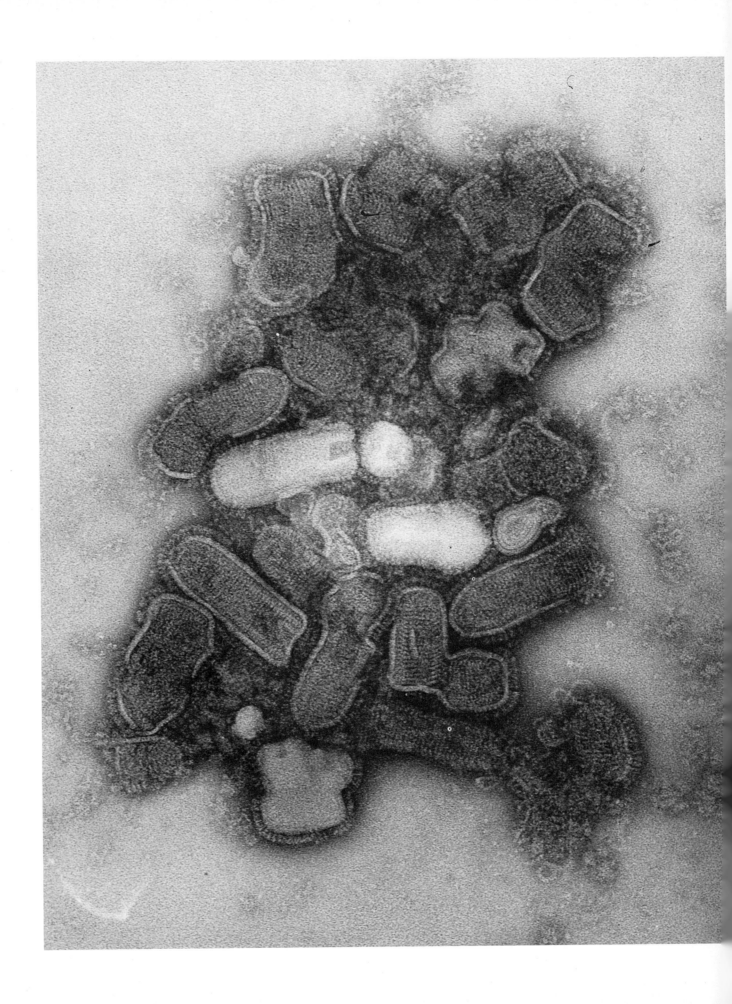

PLATE VI   VESICULAR STOMATITIS VIRUS   ×320,000

RNA, single-stranded, 6 percent

Helical, bullet-shaped and enveloped, 65 nm diameter × 170 nm length

VESICULAR stomatitis virus (VSV) causes a disease in horses and cattle very much like foot and mouth disease, with fever, loss of appetite, excessive salivation, and vesicular lesions around the mouth. It is, however, far from being as lethal as foot and mouth disease, and recovery from its effects is fast and complete. Epidemics of vesicular stomatitis seem to start in Central America and spread north during the warm months, leading to speculation that transmission is by an insect vector. In fact, before the description of its unusual bullet-shaped form in 1962, VSV was classified as an arbovirus because of its isolation from arthropods, its multiplication in mosquitoes, and its inactivation by ether.

Unfortunately there has been considerable confusion in the nomenclature of the group of viruses to which VSV belongs. One widely used term is rhabdovirus, but it had been previously employed in many books on general virology for nonenveloped, helical RNA viruses such as PVX, TMV, and TRV. Another name, stomatoviridae, has been proposed. Its use for VSV is apt enough, but it serves poorly as a group name for the viruses of several insect and plant diseases, with widely varying symptoms, whose known relation to vesicular stomatitis appears to be only the bullet shape of the virions. The list of viruses with bullet, or bacilliform, shapes is now very extensive and includes rabies in mammals, Egtved in rainbow trout, Flanders-Hart Park in birds, Mount Elgon bat in bats, sigma in *Drosophila,* and many viruses in wheat, maize, potatoes, rice, and other plants. Vesicular stomatitis virus can infect humans who come in contact with diseased animals and sometimes produces severe symptoms.

There are two immunologically distinct types of VSV. One type was isolated in Indiana in 1925 and the other in New Jersey the following year. Strangely enough there are apparently only these two types. All other isolates have been found to be serologically either of the Indiana or New Jersey strain. The main structural features of VSV can be seen in Plate VI. The virions are bullet-shaped and come in two distinctive lengths, with the shorter ones frequently appearing in pairs. In the micrograph shown the negative stain has penetrated into the interior of most of the particles and reveals a set of striations transverse to the particle axis. One or two virions have partially disintegrated and show a ribbon-like component that is presumably the nucleocapsid. Almost all of them are surrounded by a membrane that is outwardly studded with fine projections. The longer particles are about 170 nm long and 65 nm in diameter.

According to the structural model proposed by Nakai and Howatson in 1968, the nucleoprotein of the virion is in the form of a single helix of about 30 turns capped by four or five turns of diminishing diameter at the round end. The helix consists of about 1,000 protein subunits of dimensions approximately $10 \times 3 \times 3$ nm, with the long axis of each subunit oriented along the radius of the helix, leaving a central hole about 27 nm in diameter. The nucleocapsid is about 6 percent single-stranded RNA, with a molecular weight of 3 to 4×10^6 daltons and a length of about 4 microns. It probably contributes to the continuity of the helix of protein subunits, as in the structure of tobacco mosaic virus.

Unfractionated preparations of VSV contain the two sizes of virion seen in Plate VI. The longer one is designated "B" for bullet-shaped, and the shorter one "T" for truncated. The latter form is not infectious by itself, but it is produced in infections caused by a mixture of B and T particles, or by B particles alone, in relative amounts that vary inversely with the

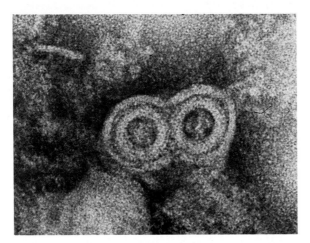

Figure 7. Electron micrograph of two T particles of vesicular stomatitis virus seen end-on. An outer envelope enclosing both virions is clearly seen. ×310,000.

dilution of the inoculum. In this respect it resembles the "von Magnus" influenza virus (Plate IV): defective virions that are deficient in RNA and are produced in abundance upon serial passage of undiluted inocula. The T particles of VSV, however, have the additional, unexplained property of interfering with the replication of the infectious B particles. Both kinds of particle are shown in Plate VI, and two T particles seen end-on are shown in Figure 7.

The spike-like surface projections and the virion envelope have been examined in the electron microscope after either trypsin or phospholipase digestion to determine what structural changes are correlated with the changes in complement-fixation activity, immunizing activity, and infectivity that result from enzyme treatment. It seems likely that the spike-like structure is a glycoprotein involved in the attachment of the virus to the cell membrane and also responsible for producing neutralizing antibodies. It is an entirely virus-specific protein and may be attached directly to the internal helical structure of the virus. There is also a phospholipid structural component, apparently derived from the cells during virus maturation, that is believed to be located in the regions between the spikes.

Early stages of entry of VSV into host cells are apparently much like those of other membrane-enclosed viruses, such as Sendai and influenza. The fusion of the viral and the host cell membranes is followed by release of the nucleocapsid core directly into the cytoplasm. After the synthesis of the nucleoprotein of the virus progeny there is an accumulation in the cytoplasm of inclusions of filamentous strands. These strands are the ribonucleoprotein of VSV and are found near the cytoplasmic membrane where the virions emerge by a budding process. Budding virus particles are seen as fingerlike projections consisting of a dense, striated core enveloped in a membrane that is continuous with the cell membrane. Sometimes two or more cores are extruded in tandem within a single envelope.

Selected Bibliography

Cartwright, B., Smale, C. J., and Brown, F.: Surface structure of vesicular stomatitis virus. *J Gen Virol, 5:* 1, 1969.

Heine, J. W., and Schnaitman, C. A.: Entry of vesicular stomatitis virus into L cells. *J Virol, 8:* 786, 1971.

Howatson, A. F.: Vesicular stomatitis and related viruses. *Adv Virus Res, 16:* 195, 1970.

Howatson, A. F., and Whitmore, G. F.: The development and structure of vesicular stomatitis virus. *Virology, 16:* 466, 1962.

Mudd, J. A., and Summers, D. F.: Protein synthesis in vesicular stomatitis virus-infected HeLa cells. *Virology, 42:* 328, 1970.

Nakai, T., and Howatson, A. F.: The fine structure of vesicular stomatitis virus. *Virology, 35:* 268, 1968.

Zajac, B. A., and Hummeler, K.: Morphogenesis of the nucleoprotein of vesicular stomatitis virus. *J Virol, 6:* 243, 1970.

PLATE VII

BACTERIOPHAGE MS2

x 330,000

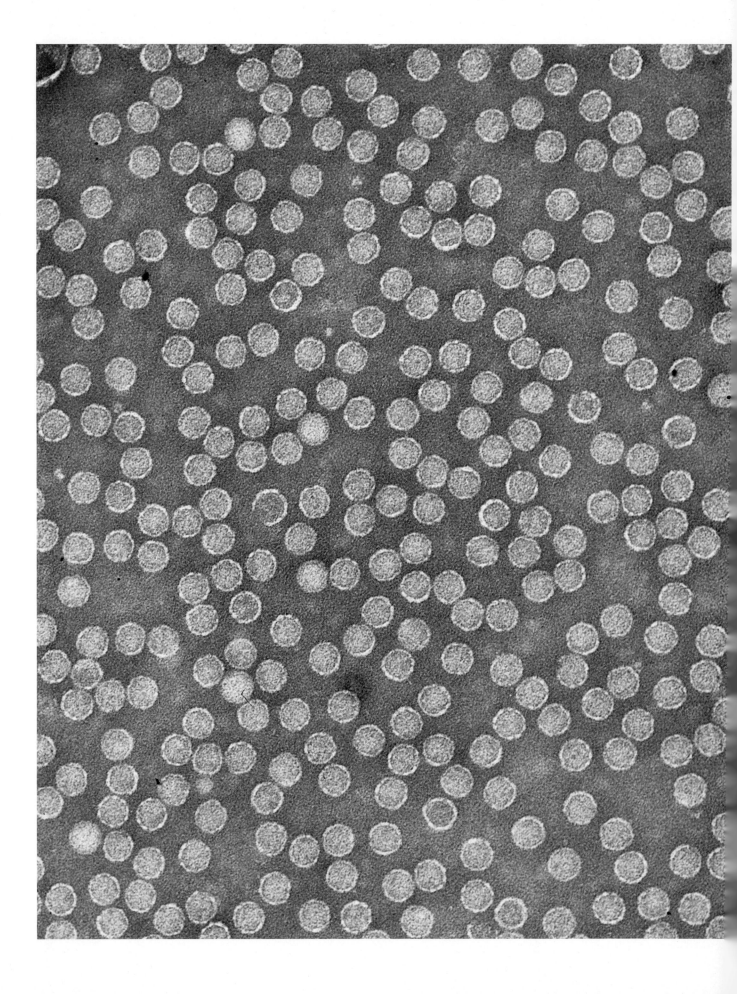

PLATE VII BACTERIOPHAGE MS2 x330,000

RNA, single-stranded, 32 percent

Isometric (icosahedral?), 35 nm

Iₙ 1961 Loeb and Zinder discovered a type of bacterial virus previously not known nor anticipated: a small, isometric virus containing single-stranded RNA. Until this time all bacteriophages had been found to contain DNA, either single- or double-stranded. This new virus, termed f2, infected only male strains of *Escherichia coli* K12. Since 1961 several similar RNA-containing bacteriophages have been found. The group containing f2 also includes MS2, R17, and fr; a less closely related species is called Qβ.

All known RNA phages infect only the male strain of *Escherichia coli* K12, and all do so by initial attachment to the thread-like appendages of these cells, called the pili. They apparently release their RNA and A-protein (see below) at this time and then de-adsorb from the pilus as an empty protein shell. By some obscure mechanism the RNA finds its way to the bacterial interior, possibly by transport through the central tube of the pilus. New virions are subsequently formed in abundance, with burst yields as high as 5,000 per bacterium being not uncommon.

The structure of MS2, f2, R17, and Qβ (Figs. 8 and 9) is quite similar at the electron microscopic level of size. Intact particles show some sign of capsomeric structure, but the number of capsomers is difficult to discern. It has been proposed that the number is 32, implying that the capsid structure has a triangulation number T = 3, with the capsomers arranged as hexons and pentons. Such a structure would have 180 structural subunits that might be identifiable with the protein subunits. This number seems reasonable, since 1/180 of the weight of the protein portion of the whole phage is close to the weight of one monomer of protein (13,-750 daltons). The RNA of MS2 contains about 3,000 nucleotides, believed to be enough to code for just three proteins: the capsid pro-

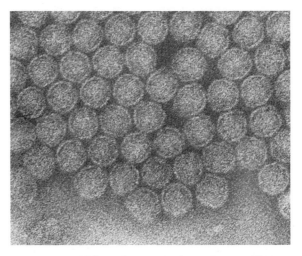

Figure 8. Virions of bacteriophage R17. ×330,000.

tein, the maturation protein ("A-protein"), and the RNA polymerase. There is just one molecule of the histidine-containing A-protein per phage particle. It seems to have an important role in the infection process, since phage mutants that lack this protein will not adsorb to the pili of the male cells. Shortly after adsorption, during the RNAse-sensitive phase of the infection cycle, the A-protein is de-adsorbed

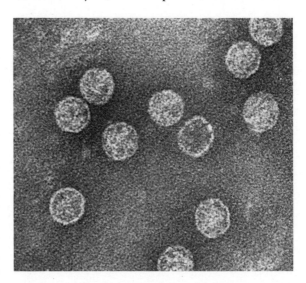

Figure 9. Virions of bacteriophage Qβ. ×320,000.

from the pilus. It is then found in solution, but no longer integrated into the phage's capsid structure.

It has been found in recent years that the virions of the RNA phages can be assembled *in vitro*. The first attempts made use of coat protein isolated by the acetic acid method and RNA isolated by phenol extraction. When these were mixed together under appropriate conditions particles were found which morphologically resembled those of RNA phages. They contained a normal RNA complement and a normal buoyant density in CsCl (1.43 gm/ml), but they lacked almost all adsorptive power to bacterial pili with consequent infectivity, and they were not RNAse-resistant. In these respects they resembled the defective particles of amber A-mutants formed *in vivo*. If purified A-protein in abundance is added to the assembly reaction mixture the particles formed are about 1,000-fold more infectious than those assembled from protein which has been isolated by acetic acid. This method of isolation does not preserve the A-protein. Even these much improved phage particles, however, have only about 10 percent of the specific infectivity of normal particles produced *in vivo*. This relatively poor showing is in contrast to the results of assembly of TMV and certain plant viruses, where almost 100 percent infectivity is obtained after *in vitro* assembly. But the latter are two-component systems only—RNA and homogeneous protein—whereas the RNA phage must contain not only its structural capsid protein but also one molecule of A-protein. It may be that, in the best reconstitution experiments, only 10 percent of the particles contain this one molecule in the correct position. As with TMV protein, the protein of the RNA phages has a tendency to self-assembly in the absence of its specific RNA, since noninfectious particles are found to be formed when protein is mixed with some nonhomologous RNA's and even in the absence of any RNA.

In 1965 Spiegelman and collaborators showed for the first time that biologically competent RNA molecules could be synthesized *in vitro*. When Qβ phage infects a cell the first protein

synthesized is an RNA polymerase, or *replicase*. This enzyme was extracted from infected cells and highly purified. Qβ RNA was extracted from whole virions by phenol extraction and highly purified. When these two components were mixed, along with the four necessary ribosetriphosphates and Mg²⁺, it was found that a net increase in RNA polymers resulted. The product was infectious when assayed on bacterial spheroplasts. (Spheroplasts were used to bypass the normal requirement that the whole virion must adsorb to the bacterial pili.) To eliminate the possibility that the infectivity was merely due to the residual infectivity of the RNA starting material, a series of dilution experiments was performed. In these, the RNA for each successive synthesis reaction was a small aliquot of the product from the reaction that preceded it. Since the specific infectivity of the RNA remained constant through 15 such dilutions it was safely concluded that new and infectious RNA was being made. When other RNA's were used as template there was no net production of RNA. Thus, it appears that Qβ replicase is highly specific in its choice of substrate and that the *in vivo* synthesis of biologically active RNA requires no mysterious material other than the polymerase molecule.

Selected Bibliography

Hohn, T.: Selfassembly of defective particles of the bacteriophage fr. *Eur J Biochem, 2:* 152, 1967.

Hohn, T., and Hohn, B.: Structure and assembly of simple RNA bacteriophages. *Adv Virus Res, 16:* 43, 1970.

Oriel, P. J., and Cleveland, P. H.: Reassembly of bacteriophage MS2 protein from 9 M urea. *Virology, 42:* 1007, 1970.

Paranchych, W., Ainsworth, S. K., Dick, A. J., and Krahn, P. M.: Stages in phage R17 infection. V. Phage eclipse and the role of F pili. *Virology, 45:* 615, 1971.

Roberts, J. W., and Steitz, J. E. A.: The reconstitution of infective bacteriophage R17. *Proc Natl Acad Sci USA, 58:* 1416, 1967.

Spiegelman, S., Pace, N. R., Mills, D. R., Levisohn, R., Eikhom, T. S., Taylor, M. M., Peterson, R. L., and Bishop, D. H. L.: The mechanism of RNA replication. *Cold Spring Harbor Symp Quant Biol, 33:* 101, 1968.

Valentine, R. C., Ward, R., and Strand, M.: The replication cycle of RNA bacteriophages. *Adv Virus Res, 15:* 1, 1969.

PLATE VIII

TURNIP YELLOW MOSAIC VIRUS

x 270,000

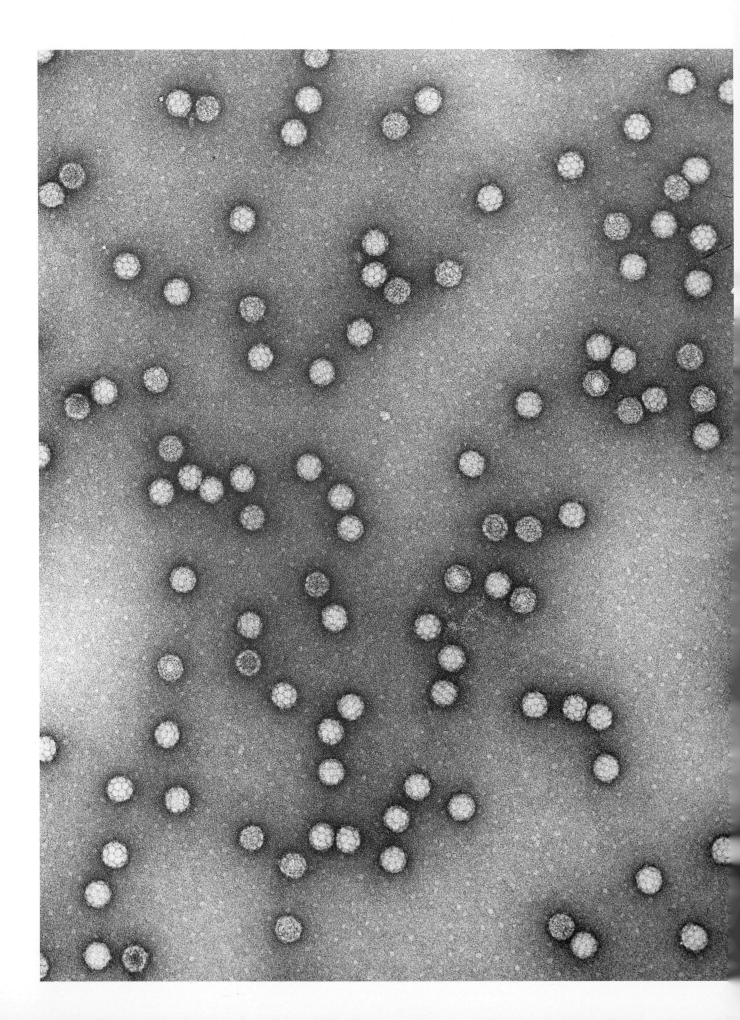

PLATE VIII   TURNIP YELLOW MOSAIC
VIRUS   x 270,000

RNA, single-stranded, 35 percent

Isometric (icosahedral), 30 nm

THE MANY INTERESTING properties of turnip yellow mosaic virus (TYMV) were first brought to the attention of virologists in 1949 when R. Markham and K. M. Smith completed a study on the transmissibility of the virus and on its chemical and physical properties. As the name implies, TYMV produces yellow patches and vein-clearing on its primary natural host, the turnip, and on its commonly used experimental host, the Chinese cabbage. Its host range appears to be limited to the *Cruciferae* family of plants. In the sap of infected Chinese cabbage it may be present in concentrations as high as 1 gm per liter.

When TYMV was first purified it was unexpectedly found that there were two classes of particle which separated in the centrifuge according to their densities. The so-called "bottom" component contains about 35 percent RNA and is infectious, while the "top" component has no RNA or infectivity. Both are found in abundance in the expressed sap of infected plants, showing that the top component is not simply a minor contaminant, although its relative amount is a function of the growth conditions of the virus. It is generally agreed, although not proved, that it exists in the infected cells and is not just an artifact of preparation. The RNA of the infectious component is readily extractable, particularly with 35 percent cold ethanol, a property unique to TYMV. Physical measurements, as well as chemical analyses, indicate that the infectious and the noninfectious components differ only by the presence or absence of RNA. The molecular weight of the former has been extensively determined and has been set at 5.5×10^6 daltons. That of the latter component has been measured to be 3.6×10^6 daltons. The difference could be accounted for by an RNA content of 1.9×10^6 daltons, the value found for it by sedimentation analysis.

The structure of the virions of TYMV has been extensively studied by x-ray analysis and by electron microscopy, with complete agreement in results. The former method showed that the virions have icosahedral point-group symmetry, i.e. axes of 5-fold, 3-fold, and 2-fold symmetry intersect at the center of the isometric particle. Klug and associates have found morphological detail in negatively stained particles arrayed in patterns such as to disclose their symmetry. The most noticeable pattern (discernible in Plate VIII) is a diamond shape, brought about by in-register superposition of capsomers on the bottom and top of the particle. Particularly from this pattern, and from the existence of 5-coordinated and 6-coordinated capsomers on particles not showing the diamond array, it was deduced that the virion has 32 morphological units. These may be thought of as arrayed on the six 5-fold symmetry axes possessed by a pentagonal dodecahedron (12 capsomers) and on the ends of the 10 axes where three adjacent pentagons join (20 capsomers). In the system of Caspar and Klug the virion of TYMV belongs to the $T = 3$ class.

Since the number of structural units in the capsid of a virus with icosahedral symmetry must be 60 T, it follows that TYMV has 180 of them. It may be concluded that the structural unit is actually the protein monomer in the capsid. Quantitative amino acid analysis yields 20,000 daltons for the weight of the protein subunit; hence the entire capsid (the non-RNA part of the virion) should weigh $180 \times 20,000 = 3.6 \times 10^6$ daltons, the figure found by sedimentation analysis for the intact virion *minus* its RNA. X-ray and electron microscopic analyses have given strong hints that the viral RNA is not simply stuffed in the virion core, but that it winds to some extent through each of the 32 protruding capsomers.

31

Some methods of extraction of the viral RNA produce fragmented RNA whose average weight is about 1/32 that of the entire chain; this fragmentation may be related to the 32 sharp convolutions of the RNA in the intact virion.

While the RNA of TYMV is readily isolated in intact form, the isolation of water-soluble protein monomers can be accomplished only by methods which prevent oxidation of the four free-SH groups in the monomer. Attempts have been numerous, but unsuccessful, to reconstitute TYMV from its RNA and protein components. However, it has proved possible to "reconstitute" a hybrid "virus" by combining the RNA from TYMV with the protein subunits of TMV. A rod-like particle results, appearing like TMV, and this particle has some infectivity—causing the plant to produce TYMV progeny.

Selected Bibliography

Caspar, D. L. D., and Klug, A.: Physical principles in the construction of regular viruses. *Cold Spring Harbor Symp Quant Biol, 27:* 1, 1962.

Finch, J. T., and Klug, A.: Arrangement of protein subunits and the distribution of nucleic acid in turnip yellow mosaic virus. II. Electron microscopic studies. *J Mol Biol, 15:* 344, 1966.

Klug, A., Longley, W., and Leberman, R.: Arrangement of protein subunits and the distribution of nucleic acid in turnip yellow mosaic virus. I. X-ray diffraction studies. *J Mol Biol, 15:* 315, 1966.

Markham, R., and Smith, K. M.: Studies on the virus of turnip yellow mosaic. *Parasitology, 39:* 330, 1949.

Matthews, R. E. F., and Ralph, R. K.: Turnip yellow mosaic virus. *Adv Virus Res, 12:* 273, 1966.

PLATE IX

SATELLITE TOBACCO NECROSIS VIRUS

x 330,000

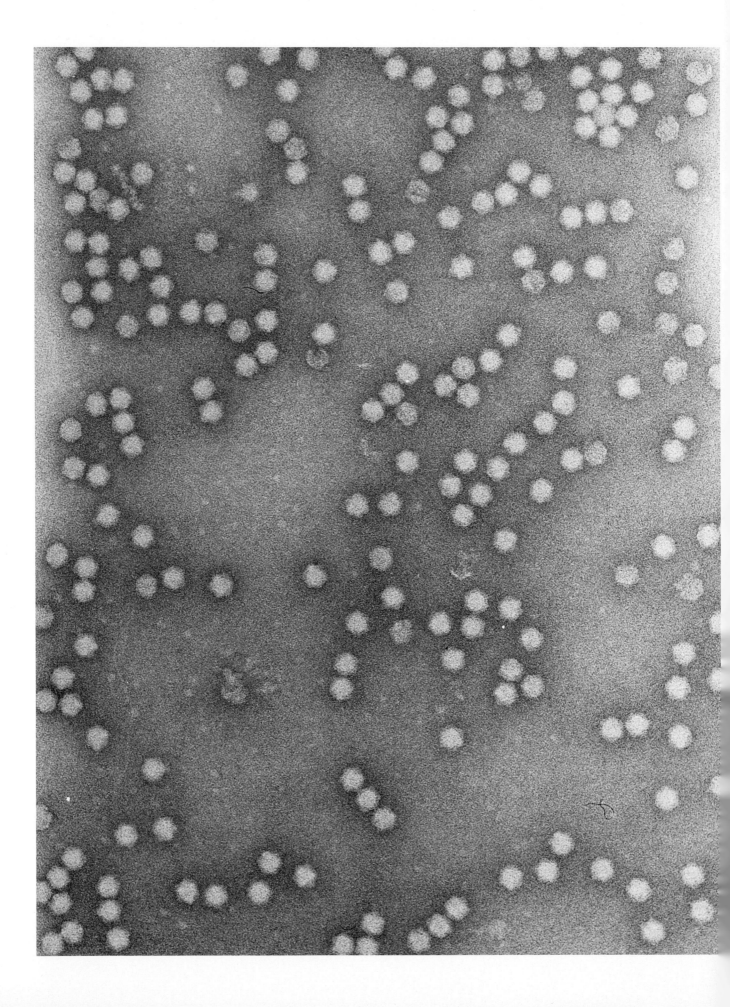

PLATE IX   SATELLITE TOBACCO NECROSIS
VIRUS   x 330,000

RNA, single-stranded, 20 percent

Isometric (icosahedral?), 18 nm

MANY PLANT VIRUSES have been found to display more than one component when they are examined in the ultracentrifuge. An example of this characteristic is tobacco necrosis virus, isolates of which were noted as long ago as 1938 to show two sedimentation boundaries, one at about 115S and one at 50S. The significance of this early observation was clarified in 1961 when Kassanis and Nixon discovered that the material from the two sedimenting species had quite distinctive properties. The heavier component was found to be identical in both its symptomological and antigenic properties with what had been called tobacco necrosis virus (TNV). The lighter component, named satellite tobacco necrosis virus (STNV) in 1962, had properties that were unprecedented. It was always present, in varying abundance, in normal TNV isolates; it was antigenically unrelated to its companion TNV; although it was a nucleoprotein found in infectious material, it was by itself incapable of initiating infection. It was subsequently discovered that not all isolates of TNV need contain STNV. If care is taken to inoculate only with the 115S component, only that species is found in purified preparations. Thus, the TNV-STNV relation is a classical example of *helper* and *defective* viruses; the latter is replicated in the host cell only when the former is also within the cell.

Tobacco necrosis virus is physically and chemically an ordinary plant virus, a nucleoprotein particle with a diameter of about 30 nm and containing about 20 percent RNA (1.6×10^6 daltons). But STNV is only 18 nm in diameter (see Fig. 10 for comparison with TNV), and while it also contains 20 percent RNA, its RNA complement is only 0.4×10^6 daltons. This small amount provides for no more than 1,200 nucleotides. Since STNV is serologically unrelated to TNV's of all known

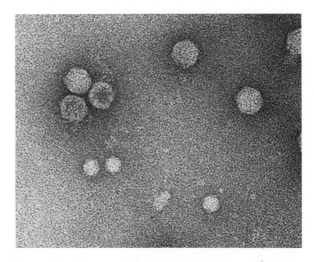

Figure 10. Electron micrograph showing a comparison in size between the particles of satellite tobacco necrosis virus and those of the larger tobacco necrosis virus. ×250,000.

strains, it is highly unlikely that the RNA of either serves in coding for the coat protein of the other. Tobacco necrosis virus RNA probably has the capacity to do so, but with STNV RNA such capability would be marginal. The coat protein of STNV has a molecular weight, most recently determined to be 23,800 daltons, requiring a little more than half the RNA for its coding. The function of the remainder of the RNA is still unknown. It is unlikely that it codes for a polymerase, since in that event it would seem that STNV would be able to function like a virus on its own.

The natural origin of STNV is a mystery. But it would seem that at some time it became associated in infected cells with TNV. The latter provided for its replication, presumably by coding for the necessary RNA polymerase, and in the process of natural transmission from host to host the parasitic particle frequently went along with the other. Its abundance in isolates from natural infections varies enormously, from zero to as much as a 100-fold predominance, in particle numbers, over TNV. For some unknown reason, in infections containing both kinds of particle there are two sizes of necrotic lesions, with the larger being more abundant in infections containing greater proportions of TNV. As mentioned before, it is possible to inoculate with only TNV or STNV. The former inoculum produces only large lesions and only TNV particles; the latter produces no symptoms and no distinctive, purifiable material. Similar results are obtained after inoculation with the RNA's; only an inoculum of mixed RNA from TNV and STNV will produce mixed lesions and both types of particle.

With its molecular weight of 23,800 daltons the protein subunit of STNV should exist in 69 copies in each virion. This is a number that does not fit into the assembly of viruses by either quasi- or full-equivalence, where only 60, or a multiple of 60, identical protein molecules are permitted. The source of this discrepancy most likely lies in the determination of the molecular weight of the protein subunit. The morphological substructure of STNV could consist of 60 equivalently located molecules, which would most likely produce a smoothly spherical outline in electron micrographs. But the contour appears hexagonal (Plate IX), indicating that the arrangement of subunits is $T = 1$, with the protein molecules clustered into a pentamer at each of the 12 icosahedral vertices.

Attempts have been made to assess the function of the RNA of STNV by investigating its translational activity. Translating systems from both *Escherichia coli* and wheat embryo extracts have been used. The results show that a protein is translated which is almost identical with that produced by STNV RNA *in vivo*. No sign of any other polypeptide has appeared, making it seem likely that even in the plant the RNA of STNV acts as a monocistronic messenger.

Selected Bibliography

Kassanis, B.: Properties and behaviour of a virus depending for its multiplication on another. *J Gen Microbiol, 27:* 477, 1962.

Kassanis, B.: Properties and behaviour of satellite virus. *Proc Int Conf Plant Viruses, Wageningen 1965,* pp. 177–187, 1966.

Kassanis, B., and Nixon, H. L.: Activation of one tobacco necrosis virus by another. *J Gen Microbiol, 25:* 459, 1961.

Klein, W. H., Nolan, C., Lazar, J. M., and Clark, J. M., Jr.: Translation of satellite tobacco necrosis virus ribonucleic acid. I. Characterization of *in vitro* procaryotic and eucaryotic translation products. *Biochemistry, 11:* 2009, 1972.

Rees, M. W., Short, M. N., and Kassanis, B.: The amino acid composition, antigenicity, and other characteristics of the satellite viruses of tobacco necrosis viruses. *Virology, 40:* 448, 1970.

Reichmann, M. E.: The satellite tobacco necrosis virus: A single protein and its genetic code. *Proc Natl Acad Sci USA, 52:* 1009, 1964.

PLATE X

BROME MOSAIC VIRUS

x 300,000

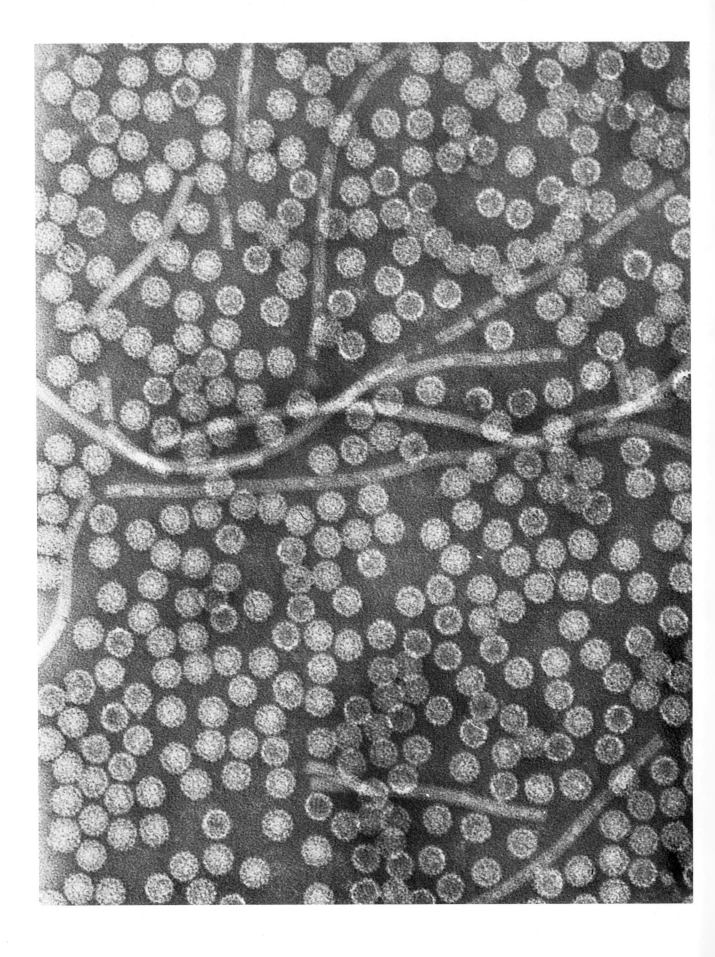

PLATE X   BROME MOSAIC VIRUS   x 300,000

RNA, single-stranded, 22 percent
Isometric (icosahedral), 25 nm

BROME MOSAIC VIRUS (BMV), a natural pathogen of bromegrass, is one of a small group of plant viruses having common structural characteristics. The virions are small in size (about 25 nm in diameter), have a capsid that is built with the same arrangement of subunits, and contain single-stranded, multi-component RNA. Two other members of this group are cowpea chlorotic mosaic virus (CCMV) and broad bean mottle virus (BBMV). The capsids of these viruses are made up of capsomers arranged in a $T = 3$ pattern: 180 protein subunits clustered in 20 hexamers and 12 pentamers to give 32 morphological units. This is the kind of array exhibited by several of the small RNA viruses, such as, for example, turnip yellow mosaic virus (Plate VIII). The whole virion of BMV has a weight of 4.6×10^6 daltons, of which 22 percent is RNA. The protein subunits have a weight of 20,000 daltons, determined by chemical analysis; this figure is satisfyingly the same as that obtained by dividing the total weight of the protein of the virion $(3.6 \times 10^6$ daltons) by the number of subunits in the capsid (180).

When BMV is sedimented in a density gradient it is found to form a band that is broader than what might be expected, in view of the high degree of uniformity shown by BMV virions in the electron microscope (Plate X). Such heterogeneity of density, of course, suggests that the virions in the population do not all have the same amounts, or kinds, of RNA. It was noted several years ago that if samples are taken from the leading, and trailing, edge of the band and separately assayed on host plants, the specific infectivity in the samples is markedly less than that of a preparation that pooled the two. Thus, a cooperative situation was indicated, one in which virions containing different amounts of RNA had to be present in an inoculum to achieve maximal infectivity.

In 1971, Lane and Kaesberg found by electrophoretic analysis that the RNA of BMV comes in four sizes: 1.09, 0.99, 0.75 and 0.28×10^6 daltons (designated as components 1 to 4). These RNA species could be associated with three distinguishable species of virion, based on small density differences. The *heavy* and the *light* particles contain, respectively, only RNA components 1 and 2, while the *medium* particles contain both components 3 and 4. Infectivity tests of the isolated RNA's showed that infectivity was achieved only if components 1, 2, and 3 were all present, the first demonstration of the existence of a multiple genome in an apparently homogeneous virus. This finding explained the earlier observations on the infectivity distribution in the bands of density-sedimented whole virions; a mixture of material from two separated portions of the band would be more likely to include virions of all the three required densities than would material from a single region.

The role of component 4 of the RNA of BMV is a mystery. It is not required for infectivity, but it may have a structural function since it is always found in medium-density virions even when inoculations have been made in its absence. It must derive from one of the larger RNA components, since it is not self-replicating. Component 3 seems to be the one that serves as parent. Tests for RNA messenger function in cell-free systems show that both components 3 and 4 contain the cistron for translation of the viral coat protein. It is also found that component 3 contains all of the nucleotide sequence of component 4. The latter clearly derives from the larger RNA, but since it seems to have no function for which it is uniquely responsible, its existence is puzzling.

A most interesting property of the group of viruses that includes BMV is their ready susceptibility to disassembly and to *in vitro* reassembly. The binding forces between the protein subunits and between these molecules and the RNA are evidently much weaker than those obtaining in tobacco mosaic virus where rather extreme conditions are required to separate protein from RNA. Simple exposure of BMV, or CCMV, to a pH above 7.0 will, in the absence of a divalent cation, cause the virions to swell and to become relatively noninfectious. Readjustment to pH < 6.0 will shrink the virions to their normal size, but will not restore infectivity, presumably because scission of the RNA has occurred during swelling. If a ribonuclease is added to the preparation of swollen virions, at pH > 7.0, the RNA is degraded and the protein released in its monomeric form. At this time the protein may be reassembled by lowering the pH under appropriate ionic conditions. Organized aggregates are formed with a variety of forms, including wide tubes, narrow tubes, small spheres, ellipsoids and double-walled spheres, as well as spheres of the size of intact virions. Figure 11 shows examples of some of these forms. The arrangement of the capsomers in the reaggregated assemblies is mostly like

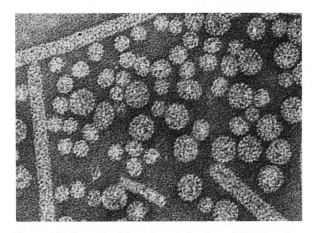

Figure 11. Cowpea chlorotic mosaic virus, following degradation and reassembly. Portions of two narrow tubes and of one wide tube are seen, as well as small spheres, and particles the size of the intact virions. ×240,000.

that of the intact virion, T = 3, but T = 1 arrangements also exist.

Like TMV and some other helical viruses, the protein and RNA of BMV (and of CCMV and BBMV) may be reconstituted to form particles with full infectivity and all the other properties found for the intact virion. But the co-assembly is quite nonspecific compared with that of TMV. For example, the proteins of the three viruses in this group and the three RNA's may be reconstituted in the nine possible protein-RNA combinations. While the infectivity yield is not the same for all combinations, the progeny virus is always genetically identical with the RNA-donating parent, and the electrophoretic mobility and antigenic properties are those of the protein-donating parent. Even quite bizarre physical reconstitution is possible: RNA's from TMV, phage f2, ribosomes, and even DNA from phage S13, have been combined with protein from one or more of these three viruses to form particles that are physically like the intact virions of the starting material. More interesting, perhaps, is the demonstration of *in vitro* phenotypic mixing: Protein from CCMV and BMV, when mixed, will reconstitute with the RNA of either to yield particles with electrophoretic mobility and antigenic behavior intermediate between those of the two viruses.

Selected Bibliography

Bancroft, J. B.: The self-assembly of spherical plant viruses. *Adv Virus Res, 16:* 99, 1970.

Bockstahler, L. E., and Kaesberg, P.: The molecular weight and other biophysical properties of bromegrass mosaic virus. *Biophys J, 2:* 1, 1962.

Lane, L. C., and Kaesberg, P.: Multiple genetic components in bromegrass mosaic virus. *Nature* [*New Biol*], *232:* 40, 1971.

Shih, D.-S., Lane, L. C., and Kaesberg, P.: Origin of the small component of brome mosaic virus RNA. *J Mol Biol, 64:* 353, 1972.

PLATE XI

POLIOVIRUS

x 320,000

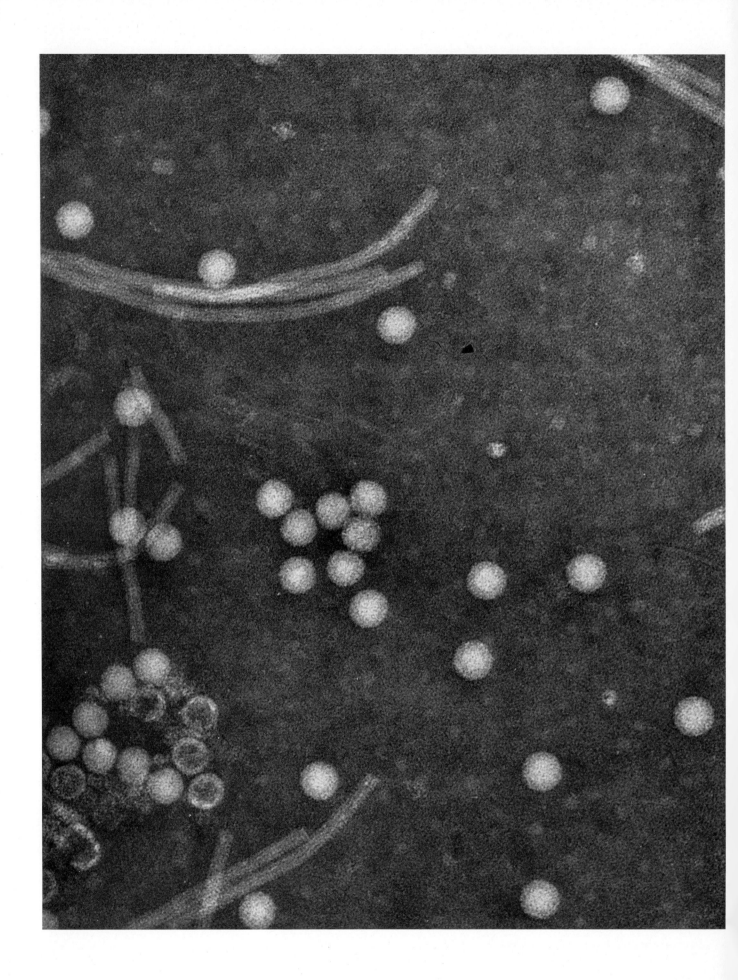

PLATE XI   POLIOVIRUS   x320,000

RNA, single-stranded, 29 percent

Isometric (icosahedral), 28 nm

POLIOMYELITIS, a virus disease for which humans are the only natural hosts, frequently involves the central nervous system and results in paralysis and deformity of the victim. Although the long-term persistence of poliomyelitis in the human population is attested to by records that go back five thousand years, it rose and fell as a significant public health problem within the first sixty years of this century. The disease is usually relatively mild in infants, but the probability of neural involvement with consequent paralysis is increased in older children and young adults. Paradoxically, prior to the improved level of sanitary conditions in the late 1800's it is likely that almost everyone had poliomyelitis in early childhood, thus receiving permanent immunity without a high incidence of crippling effects. During the early years of this century, however, the population was no longer generally immune and the disease increasingly attacked older children and young adults, in whom its paralytic aftermath was pathetic. It was originally known as "infantile paralysis," but later was given the name "poliomyelitis," from "polio," meaning grey, and "myel," meaning marrow. This later name originated from the observation that cells in the grey marrow of the spinal cord were frequently destroyed.

During the early decades of this century the onset of summer was the onset of the poliomyelitis season, with thousands of disease victims in the United States alone. Former President Franklin D. Roosevelt incurred poliomyelitis in young adulthood and was afterward incapable of walking unaided. Because of the attention which this specific case brought, and the visual impact of thousands of crippled children, a volunteer organization called the National Foundation for Infantile Paralysis was formed to fight the disease. A novel association for this purpose was made among the Foundation,

the U.S. government, the pharmaceutical industry and hundreds of biomedical scientists. As a result of their efforts an effective vaccine was developed and administered, reducing the incidence of polio from an average of about 30,000 victims per year to a figure close to zero.

The successful development of a polio vaccine depended upon the results of several key studies: (1) It was found that three different types, or strains, of the virus existed with different antigenic properties; (2) mass production of the virus in primate tissue culture became possible; (3) a means was developed for inactivating the infective part of the virus with formaldehyde while preserving antigenicity (the "Salk vaccine"); and (4) attenuated strains of the virus were developed, strains which were not overtly pathogenic but were capable of producing long-lasting immunity (the oral "Sabin vaccine").

During the 1950's the physical and chemical properties of poliovirus were actively studied. Its crystallization in 1955 by Schwerdt and Schaffer marked the first crystallization of an animal virus (Fig. 12). The crystals obtained after long storage at 4°C were isometric, or

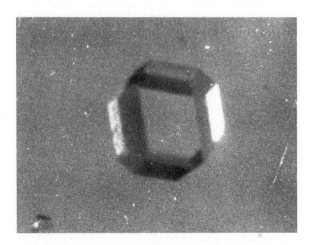

Figure 12. Light micrograph of a crystal of purified poliovirus. ×1,500.

Figure 13. A replica of a portion of a freeze-fractured crystal of poliovirus. Two crystal planes are shown; the light strip is a step region between these planes. ×150,000.

nearly so. Steere showed by electron microscopy of replicas of fractured frozen crystals (Fig. 13) that the virions were packed in the crystals in a face-centered cubic lattice. X-ray analysis of crystalline material showed unequivocally that the capsids of the virions possessed icosahedral symmetry.

Poliovirus is in the group of small, nonenveloped, animal RNA viruses called picornaviruses, all of which have similar structural properties. There are two subgroups: the enteroviruses, found primarily in the enteric tract, and the rhinoviruses, found primarily in the nasal passages. In addition to polioviruses, the Coxsackie viruses and echoviruses are in the enterovirus subgroup. The virions seen in Plate XI have a diameter of 28 nm, with some slight indications of a hexagonal contour. The capsomeric arrangement is not evident from electron micrographs, but it is very likely, on the following chemical grounds, that it has a $T = 3$ icosahedral surface lattice. The particle weight of the virion, calculated from its sedimentation coefficient of 160S, and its known shape and size, is about 6.8×10^6 daltons. The RNA content is 29 percent; hence the protein in the capsid has a weight of 6.8×10^6 *minus* 2.0×10^6, or 4.8×10^6 daltons. In an icosahedral lattice this amount of protein must be divided into 60 T subunits. The molecular weight of the protein subunit has been found to be 27,000 daltons, and the quotient obtained by dividing

4.8×10^6 daltons by this number is very close to 180. Thus it appears that the capsid of poliovirus is built in a $T = 3$ lattice. The capsomeric pattern of the virion should be visible in electron micrographs, if the subunit clustering is hexameric and pentameric, as it is in turnip yellow mosaic virus (Plate VIII). But the clustering in the poliovirus capsid may be dimeric (like tomato bushy stunt virus, Plate XII) or trimeric, in which case the capsomers might be too small to be detectable.

Poliovirus is a model example of how a ribovirus multiplies in the cytoplasm of an infected cultured cell. The cytoplasmic site has been demonstrated by autoradiographic studies with tritium-labeled uridine, by electron microscopy of the intracellular viral particles, and by microsurgery in which bits of cytoplasm from infected cells have been shown to continue to produce more poliovirus. The biosynthetic activities which come after attachment, penetration and uncoating of poliovirus involve three main sequential parts: early protein (enzyme) synthesis, progeny viral RNA synthesis, and late structural protein synthesis. The single-stranded RNA of poliovirus must serve as template in viral RNA replication and as messenger for all virus-specific protein synthesis. During the first three hours after infection the cytoplasmic smooth membranes increase and form cisternae and channels in the perinuclear region of the cell, implicating these regions as active sites in the biosynthetic activities. Very shortly after infection the parental viral RNA molecule rapidly attaches to ribosomes for direct translation into several new proteins. Two of these new, noncapsid proteins produce an early and complete cessation of normal cellular synthesis of RNA and protein. Another new protein is RNA-dependent RNA polymerase (RNA synthetase) which catalyzes the replication of viral RNA.

During progeny viral RNA synthesis there are three structural forms found in the cell: the single-stranded form (ss-RNA), a complete double-stranded form (the replicative form), and a partial single-stranded and double-stranded form (the replicative intermediate). The parental (positive) RNA strand serves as

Plate XI—Poliovirus   45

a template for the transcription of a complementary (negative) strand, thereby creating the double-stranded complex from which the new viral ss-RNA is formed. Unlike the ss-RNA, the replicative form is ribonuclease resistant. These biosynthetic activities take place in close association with smooth cytoplasmic membranes, and several hundred thousand new viral RNA molecules are synthesized in about three hours.

The major site of translation of viral RNA and protein synthesis is in association with rough cytoplasmic membranes. A small, 14S virus-specific structural protein can be isolated from poliovirus-infected HeLa cells, a protein that is able to self-assemble into a 73S particle. This 73S particle, when negatively stained and examined in the electron microscope, resembles the empty poliovirus capsids found in infected cells. The mature virus particles in infected cells are retained for some period of time, frequently in crystalline arrays, before rapid release by destruction of the cytoplasmic membrane.

The genome of poliovirus contains polyadenylate (polyA) covalently linked to the rest of the nucleotide chain. This homopolymer of polyA is 3'-terminal and averages about 90 nucleotides long. In the double-stranded replicative form the plus strand has polyA and the minus strand contains polyU, each at its 3'-terminus. This raises the problem that if the polyA of the plus strand is synthesized by tran-

scription, the polyU in the minus strand should be 5'-terminal. One possible explanation is that circular structures might be formed, since the 3'-termini are complementary to each other. Ring forms of the double-stranded RNA of another picornavirus, encephalomyocarditis, have been reported. However, the biological function of the polyA in viral RNA is still obscure.

Selected Bibliography

Darnell, J. E., Girard, M., Baltimore, D., Summers, D. F., and Maizel, J. V.: The synthesis and translation of poliovirus RNA. In Colter, J. S., and Paranchych, W. (Eds.): *The Molecular Biology of Viruses.* New York, Acad Pr, 1967, pp. 375–401.

Dunnebacke, T. H.: Amounts of polio and Coxsackie viruses within the separate portions of bisected cultured cells. *Virology, 16:* 392, 1962.

Enders, J. F., Weller, T. H., and Robbins, F. C.: Cultivation of the Lansing strain of poliomyelitis virus in cultures of various human embryonic tissues. *Science, 109:* 85, 1949.

Finch, J. T., and Klug, A.: Structure of poliomyelitis virus. *Nature (Lond), 183:* 1709, 1959.

Phillips, B. A.: *In vitro* assembly of poliovirus. II. Evidence for the self-assembly of 14 S particles into empty capsids. *Virology, 44:* 307, 1971.

Schaffer, F. L., and Schwerdt, C. E.: Purification and properties of poliovirus. *Adv Virus Res, VI:* 159, 1959.

Steere, R. L., and Schaffer, F. L.: The structure of crystals of purified Mahoney poliovirus. *Biochim Biophys Acta, 28:* 241, 1958.

Yogo, Y., and Wimmer, E.: Poly(A) and Poly(U) in poliovirus double stranded RNA. *Nature [New Biol], 242:* 171, 1973.

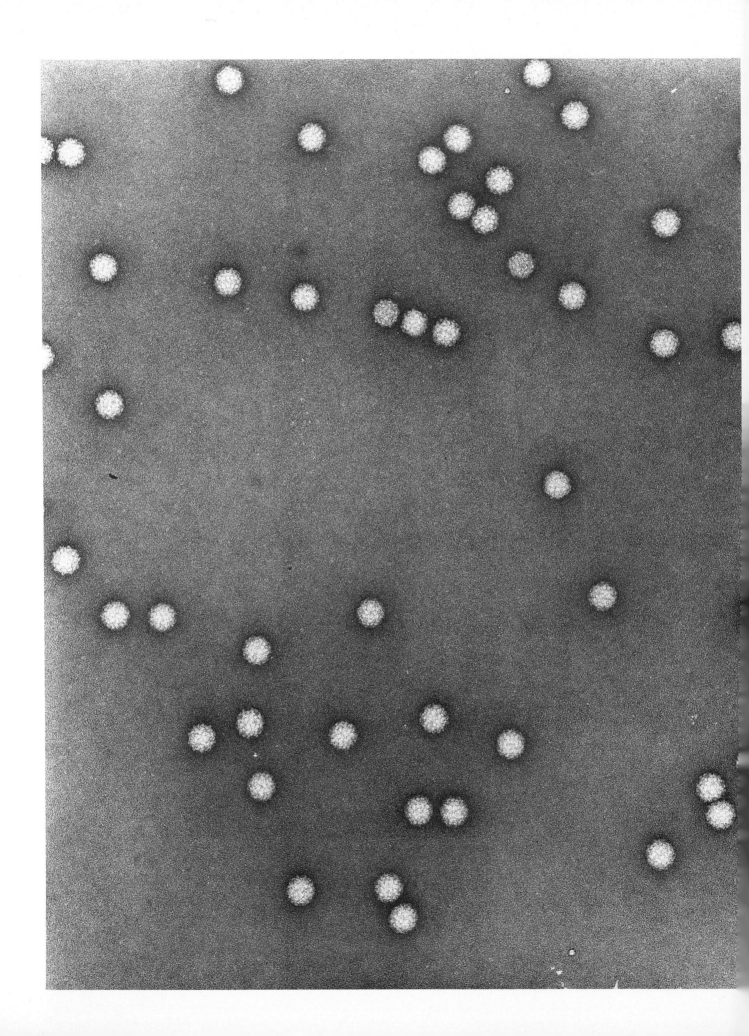

PLATE XII   TOMATO BUSHY STUNT VIRUS   x250,000

RNA, single-stranded, 17 percent

Isometric (icosahedral), 30 nm

Tomato bushy stunt virus (TBSV) was first isolated from tomato plants in 1935. A more productive laboratory host was later found to be *Datura stramonium* from which the yield of purified virus may be as high as 100 mg/liter of infected sap. In 1938 Bawden and Pirie succeeded in forming crystals of the virus which were regular in three dimensions, the first such crystallization of any virus. (Tobacco mosaic virus, first "crystallized" in 1935, forms para-crystals that are irregular in one dimension.) TBSV was also the first isometric virus to be examined by methods of x-ray crystallography. Later, in 1956, x-ray analysis showed that the virions of TBSV possessed icosahedral symmetry, the first showing that a virus can be built of subunits arrayed according to a detailed architectural plan. In the many experiments that have been performed over the years to perfect methods for measuring the molecular weights, sizes, shapes, and degree of hydration of viruses, the virions of TBSV have served as the type example of particles that are extraordinarily uniform in their physical characteristics. In more recent times the virus has been of interest mainly to investigators of virus structure; its economic importance as a pathogenic agent is negligible.

The RNA of TBSV, while not well characterized, does appear to exist in one piece within the virion. Upon extraction with phenol the RNA sediments at S $\approx$ 30, and this is a reasonable value for one single strand of RNA with a molecular weight of 1.6×10^6 daltons, the total amount known to be within the virion. Discrepant results have been obtained for the molecular weight of the protein subunit, ranging from 60,000 to 33,000 daltons, but recent determinations have been in agreement on a molecular weight of about 40,000. There has been extensive discussion as to whether TBSV is a double-shell assembly consisting of a small (diameter $\approx$ 20 nm) inner capsid, surrounded by a layer of RNA which in turn is surrounded by an outer capsid with the observed 30-nm diameter of the intact virion. This speculation arose over the circumstance that in preparations of TBSV and the related virus, turnip crinkle, RNA-free particles about 20-nm diameter are found, frequently in the former and rarely in the latter. These were thought to represent a core protein capsid, present in both viruses. Later work, discussed below, shows that the so-called core particles are most probably re-aggregation products; e.g. protein subunits of either of the two viruses, existing in the juice of infected plants or deliberately produced by disaggregation of the virions, that have spontaneously aggregated to form the smaller, RNA-free particle.

The resolution of the question about core particles has come about from electron microscopic observations combined with the more recent determinations of subunit molecular weights. Finch, Klug, and Leberman deduced from electron micrographs of TBSV that the virion contains 90 morphological units, or capsomers. This number is not compatible with any number derivable from the Caspar-Klug model of virus structure if, as had been universally found before, the structural units are clustered in hexamers and pentamers to form the observable capsomers. If, however, there is dimer clustering of the subunits, their total number (S) would be 180, a number called for in a T = 3 assembly (S = 60 T). Thus, it appears that the capsid of TBSV contains 180 identical protein molecules. This number, combined with a value of 40,000 daltons for the molecular weight of each molecule, yields 7.2×10^6 daltons as the weight of the protein portion of the virion, in very good agreement with chemical analysis. The so-called core of the virion was found to be assembled on a T = 1 lattice, in dimer clustering; hence, it contains 60 identical molecules. Since TBSV contains only a single, major protein species the molecules of the presumptive core would have a molecular weight of 40,000 daltons, yielding a total core molecular weight of 2.4×10^6 daltons. Unfortunately for the core hypothesis, this extra amount of protein cannot be accommodated in TBSV; the observed capsid of the virion, with its 180 protein molecules, accounts for all of the protein.

[Dimer clustering, for $T = 3$, brings with it a unique characteristic in the outline of a virion seen along a 5-fold axis: the particle is bordered by ten, equally spaced *spikes*. In Plate XII two particles may be found that clearly present this 10-spike outline.]

Selected Bibliography

Bawden, F. C., and Pirie, N. W.: Crystalline preparations of tomato bushy stunt virus. *Br J Exp Pathol, 19:* 251, 1938.

Butler, P. J. G.: Structures of turnip crinkle and tomato bushy stunt viruses. III. The chemical subunits: molecular weights and number of molecules per particle. *J Mol Biol, 52:* 589, 1970.

Caspar, D. L. D.: Structure of bushy stunt virus. *Nature (Lond), 177:* 475, 1956.

Finch, J. T., Klug, A., and Leberman, R.: The structures of turnip crinkle and tomato bushy stunt viruses. II. The surface structure: dimer clustering patterns. *J Mol Biol, 50:* 215, 1970.

Michelin-Lausarot, P., Ambrosino, C., Steere, R. L., and Reichmann, M. E.: The protein of some strains of tomato bushy stunt virus. *Virology, 41:* 160, 1970.

Smith, K. M.: A new virus disease of the tomato. *Ann Appl Biol, 22:* 731, 1935.

PLATE XIII

REOVIRUS

x 200,000

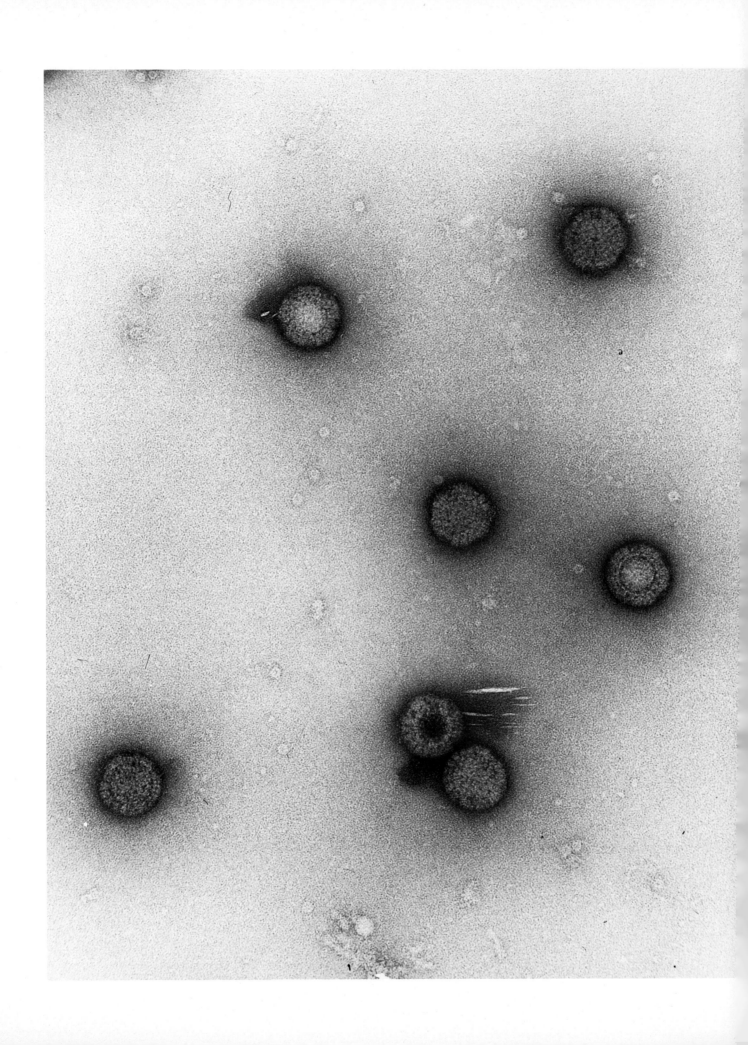

PLATE XIII   REOVIRUS   x 200,000

RNA, double-stranded, 15 percent

Isometric (icosahedral) outer shell 75 nm, core 45 nm

IN 1959 A NEW group of respiratory and enteric viruses, isolated and classified in 1954 as ECHO type 10, was described and named reovirus by A. B. Sabin. This group was easily distinguished from the numerous other enteroviruses on the basis of its large size, about 70 nm, as determined by filtration through membranes. The name, which was intended to stress the association of this virus with both the respiratory and intestinal tracts, was formed from the initial letters r and e, from the "respiratory and enteric" sites of isolation, and o standing for "orphan," since the virus could be isolated from both healthy and ill individuals. The reovirus shares some properties with members of the larger family of enteroviruses, such as cytopathogenic effects in monkey kidney tissue culture. Those cells separated from the culture flask after infection assumed a granular, degenerated appearance and contained cytoplasmic inclusions. All of the viruses in the reo-group could be isolated from human sources, a circumstance which had earlier provided the initial letters in the name ECHO (enteric, cytopathogenic, human, orphan). The reoviruses are widely distributed in nature and have been isolated from naturally infected monkeys, cattle, mice, dogs and fowl, as well as man. Although it has been suggested that it may be the agent of some disease, such as blue tongue disease in sheep, its widespread occurrence may make it difficult to associate reovirus with any human disease.

One of several interesting features of reovirus is the unusual structure of its protein capsid. This is clearly illustrated in the negatively stained reovirus particles seen in Plate XIII, where the protein shell composed of two layers of capsomers can be seen. The inner shell or core has a diameter of about 45 nm, while the diameter of the whole virion is about 75 nm. It appears to contain no lipid, a circumstance

which, together with its double-layer structure, perhaps accounts for the observed resistance of infectivity to lipid solvents and for its high thermostability. The virions can be disrupted, however, by exposure to urea and by proteolytic digestion to reveal the inner core, which then appears as a more open meshwork enclosing the viral RNA. The arrangement of the capsomers in the outer layer and in the inner core has not been established with certainty. One interpretation of the structure of the outer layer indicates the existence of 92 hollow, prismatic capsomers arranged on the surface of an icosahedron; another interpretation holds that there are 180 solid capsomers positioned equidistantly from the center of the virion and around 92 holes, while still another claims that neither of these interpretations is consistent with the presence of 20 capsomers seen on the periphery of the virion.

The structural proteins dissociated from purified virions and cores have been analyzed by sodium dodecyl sulfate (SDS)-polyacrylamide gel electrophoresis and have been shown to fall into three size classes and about seven species. The cores contain the two largest polypeptides of molecular weight 140,000 and 155,000 daltons as well as one of the smaller polypeptides of 38,000 daltons, whereas the outer shell contains intermediate polypeptides with molecular weights of 75,000 to 85,000 daltons and the smaller polypeptide of 34,000 daltons. The total weight of the protein of the reovirus capsid is about 11×10^7 daltons.

About ten years ago it was first noted that the RNA of reovirus, and of wound tumor virus (Plate XIV), might have unanticipated properties. It was first noticed that the RNA appeared in the electron microscope to have a greater diameter and was more rigid than what had been found for any other known, natural RNA. The material exhibited a hyperchromic effect upon heating, with a sharp thermal denaturation temperature, T_M, above 90° C. It was also resistant to digestion with ribonuclease. Base-ratio determinations showed molar equality of guanine and cytosine, and of adenine and uracil. All of these properties are in accord with a double-stranded, helical structure and, indeed, x-ray analysis showed a structure much like that of cellular DNA. Hence, it was concluded that the genome of reovirus and wound tumor virus is RNA in double-stranded form, unlike the single-strandedness of other known, natural RNA's. It has since been established that the reovirus genome, after extraction from the virion, is in several (perhaps ten) segments falling into three classes of size. Within the virion the segments of the genome are probably linked together into one strand of molecular weight 10.2×10^6 daltons; and they appear to remain linked during replication. Each segment is transcribed specifically into single-stranded messenger RNA by an active RNA polymerase; the polymerase activity is so great that *in vitro* transcription produces enough single-stranded RNA to allow it to be isolated and purified. It should be noted that the virions of reovirus contain not only the double-stranded RNA genome, but also a very labile single-stranded, adenine-rich RNA whose function is unknown.

The ease with which reovirus can be grown in established cell lines in tissue culture, such as HeLa and mouse L cells, has permitted extensive studies of the stages of virus replication. Adsorption and penetration apparently take place when the virus particles become enclosed within phagocytic vacuoles as they enter the cytoplasm of the host cell. These vacuoles fuse with cellular lysosomes and the reovirions become concentrated in the lysosomes of the host cell soon after penetration. The lysosomal enzymes hydrolyze the outer shell of the viral particle in a selective manner and convert the reovirions to subviral particles (SVP) of slightly higher density resembling that of the core. These SVP have sufficiently great density to permit their isolation from infected cells. The hydrolases contained within the lysosomal compartment do not degrade the viral core proteins, nor do the lysosomal nucleases degrade the double-stranded RNA, the genome within the SVP. The RNA transcriptase activity which is latent in the intact virion is activated by this removal of the outer shell, following which event the parental double-stranded RNA is transcribed. The newly synthesized single-stranded RNA messenger molecules are released from the parental subviral particle even though it remains intact throughout the replicative cycle. This single-stranded RNA acts not only as a messenger for the virus-specific protein, but also as a template for the formation of the new double-stranded RNA. The SVP can undergo recoating to complete virions by a self-assembly process that is probably one of the normal steps in the maturation process.

Selected Bibliography

Dunnebacke, T. H., and Kleinschmidt, A. K.: Ribonucleic acid from reovirus as seen in protein monolayers by electron microscopy. *Z Naturforsch, 22b:* 159, 1967.

Luftig, R. B., Kilham, S. S., Hay, A. J., Zweerink, H. J., and Joklik, W. K.: An ultrastructural study of virions and cores of reovirus type 3. *Virology, 48:* 170, 1972.

Millward, S., and Nonoyama, M.: Segmented structure of the reovirus genome. *Cold Spring Harbor Symp Quant Biol, 35:* 773, 1970.

Sabin, A. B.: Reoviruses. *Science, 130:* 1387, 1959.

Shatkin, A. J.: Replication of reovirus. *Adv Virus Res, 14:* 63, 1969.

Silverstein, S. C., Astell, C., Levin, D. H., Schonberg, M., and Acs, G.: The mechanisms of reovirus uncoating and gene activation *in vivo. Virology, 47:* 797, 1972.

Smith, R. E., Zweerink, H. J., and Joklik, W. K.: Polypeptide components of virions, top component and cores of reovirus type 3. *Virology, 39:* 791, 1969.

PLATE XIV

WOUND TUMOR VIRUS

x 260,000

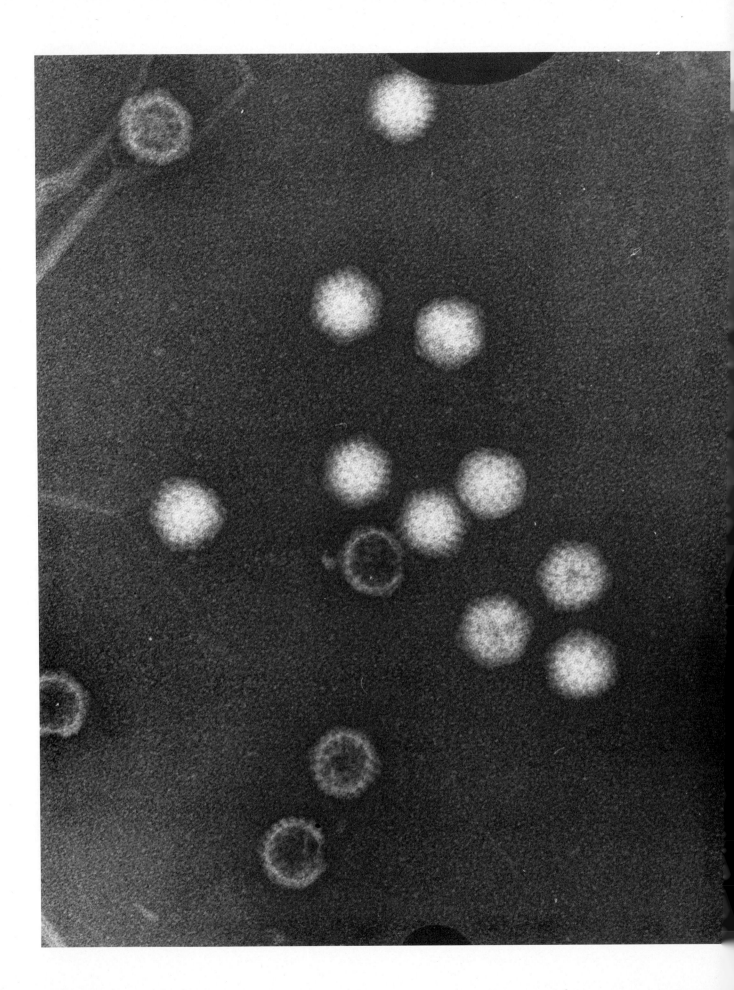

PLATE XIV   WOUND TUMOR VIRUS   x260,000

RNA, double-stranded, 20 percent

Isometric (icosahedral), 65 nm

INTERESTING possibilities for the study of neoplasia in plants were introduced in 1944 by L. M. Black with the demonstration that plant tumors could be induced by the combined action of wounds and a virus. Subsequently the viral agent which caused the growth of tumors on the roots and stems, and caused enlarged leaf veins in sweet clover *(Melilotus alba),* was named wound tumor virus (WTV). The virus has been demonstrated to produce symptoms typical of WTV in about twenty different plant families. Crimson clover *(Trifolium incarnatum)* has been extensively used as a test plant for the virus because of its suitability as a food plant for insect vectors of the virus and because of its high susceptibility and uniform expression of symptoms. Natural transmission of the wound tumor disease is through the vector of a juice-sucking leaf hopper such as *Agalliopsis novella.* However, since WTV multiplies in systemically infected insects to titers as high as those found in the plant (about 10^{12} particles per gm of tissue), the distinction that the plant is the host and the leaf hopper the vector rests solely on the grounds that the insect is mobile and shows no overt disease effects. The severity of the disease in the plant varies according to its species and age, the growth temperature, and the nature of the initial wounding. Some of these observations have led to speculation that tumor development is stimulated by a plant growth hormone released from damaged cells.

Accumulations of electron-dense aggregates are found in the cytoplasm of thin-sectioned cells of both plant and insect tissue infected with WTV. These inclusions appear characteristically as microcrystals of virions, are not bounded by a membrane, and are found only in the cytoplasm. The virus has been shown to be widespread in the tissues of infected insects including the cells of muscle, trachea, epidermis, and salivary gland; by far the largest accumulations have been found, however, in the cytoplasm of fat-body cells, implying that these cells may be a primary site for virus multiplication in the insect. Black has suggested that the natural alternate cycle of virus multiplication in a plant and in an insect, with trans-ovarian passage in the latter, indicates an exogenous origin of the virus and a long evolutionary development prior to the attainment of its refined parasitic status. These interesting implications might well be remembered in considering the human cancer problem.

The establishment of an *in vitro* cell line from *Agallia constricta,* a vector of WTV, has permitted quantitative studies not normally possible with a plant virus. Infectivity assays on the cultured vector-cell monolayers are more sensitive, more rapid, and more accurate than infectivity assays by injection of the virus into vectors which are then tested for virus content by allowing them to feed on plants. As distinct from the normal plaque assay the WTV assay involves detection of foci caused by the virus in the monolayer by staining with fluorescent antibody and counting the foci in a fluorescence microscope. The linearity of the relationship between WTV concentration and the number of foci indicates that each focus represents an infection initiated by one infective unit.

Highly purified virus preparations from the insect tissue and from the root and stem tumors of sweet clover appear identical in the electron microscope. The virus particles have been shown to be about 60 nm in diameter and to have an icosahedral shape when examined by shadowing from two directions 60 degrees apart. In negative stain the profile of the virion is frequently seen to be hexagonal (Plate XIV) with four capsomers about 7.5 nm in diameter arrayed along an edge. This capsomeric array implies that the capsid is built on a $T = 9$ lattice and contains 92 capsomers.

The genome of WTV is a double-stranded RNA with properties very similar to those of reovirus (described under Plate XIII). When extracted from the virion it is found in strands shorter than the 7 μm, or so, that would be expected if the RNA of molecular weight 15×10^6 daltons were all in one piece. Like the reovirus genome it is apparently separated into segments upon extraction. Its x-ray pattern is indistinguishable from that of reovirus. Despite the similarity in appearance of the virions and of the genomic RNA of reovirus and wound tumor virus, the two viruses share no common host nor do they have any serological cross-reaction.

Electron micrographs of negatively stained WTV occasionally show particles with a central core about 35 nm in diameter, representing 20 percent of the volume of the particle. This volume is presumably occupied by the RNA and also an associated RNA transcriptase. The enzyme is capable of transcribing single-stranded RNA from the double-stranded RNA genome and allows viral messenger RNA's to be made after the virus enters the host cell. Such messenger RNA's could be translatable differently by plant and insect host cells, thus accounting for the widely differing response in the two host systems.

Selected Bibliography

Bils, R. F., and Hall, C. E.: Electron microscopy of wound-tumor virus. *Virology, 17:* 123, 1962.

Black, D. R., and Knight, C. A.: Ribonucleic acid transcriptase activity in purified wound tumor virus. *J Virol, 6:* 194, 1970.

Black, L. M.: Physiology of virus-induced tumors in plants. In *Handbuch der Pflanzenphysiologie.* Berlin, Springer-Verlag, 1965, vol. 15, part 2, pp. 236–266.

Black, L. M., and Markham, R.: Base-pairing in the ribonucleic acid of wound-tumor virus. *Neth J Plant Pathol, 69:* 215, 1963.

Gomatos, P. J., and Tamm, I.: Animal and plant viruses with double-helical RNA. *Proc Natl Acad Sci USA, 50:* 878, 1963.

Kimura, I., and Black, L. M.: Some factors affecting infectivity assays of wound-tumor virus on cell monolayers from an insect vector. *Virology, 46:* 266, 1971.

Kleinschmidt, A. K., Dunnebacke, T. H., Spendlove, R. S., Schaffer, F. L., and Whitcomb, R. F.: Electron microscopy of RNA from reovirus and wound tumor virus. *J Mol Biol, 10:* 282, 1964.

PLATE XV
CYTOPLASMIC POLYHEDROSIS VIRUS
x 200,000

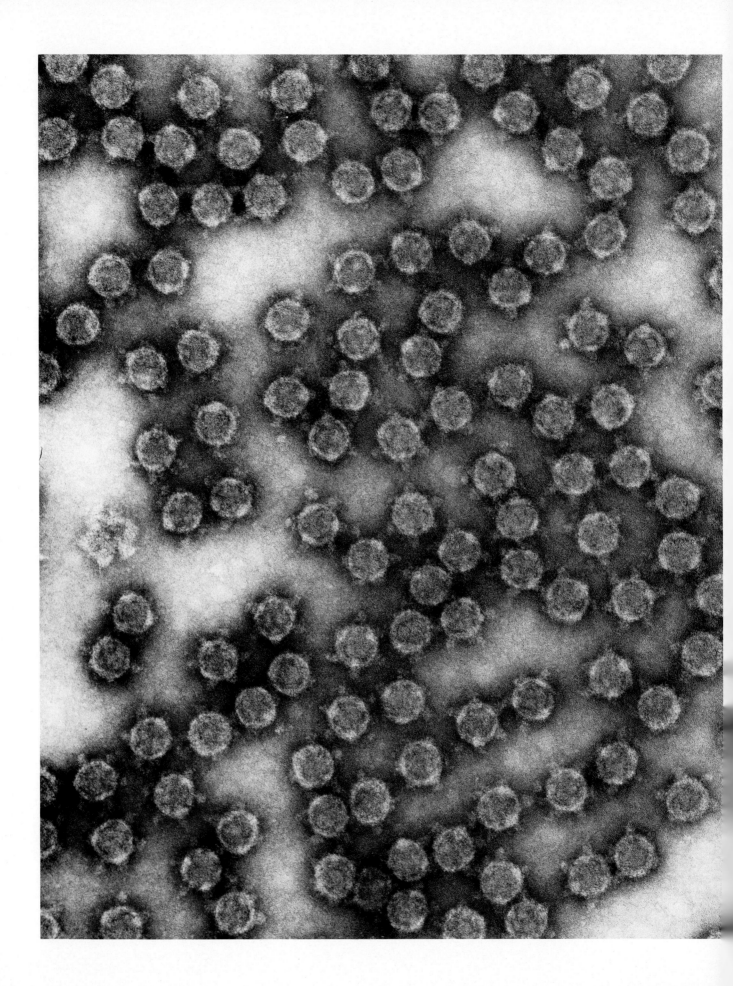

PLATE XV CYTOPLASMIC POLYHEDROSIS VIRUS x 200,000

RNA, double-stranded, 23 percent

Isometric (double-shell, icosahedral?), outer shell 60 nm, core 30 nm

FOR SEVERAL CENTURIES the cultivation of the silkworm, *Bombyx mori,* has been a major branch of agriculture, and it is still of significant economic importance in Japan. Hence, it is only natural that Japanese scientists have carried out most of the research on silkworm diseases, particularly on the most common pathogens of silkworms such as cytoplasmic polyhedrosis virus (CPV). In 1934 Ishimori first described CPV in the silkworm when he observed polyhedra in the cytoplasm of the midgut cells of a diseased larva. Since that time it has been widely observed that the shapes and sizes of the polyhedral inclusion bodies may vary greatly in different insect species, and even in a single insect species infected with polyhedrosis viruses.

Cytoplasmic polyhedrosis virus usually infects the larvae of the silkworm, but the pupa and adult can also be infected. If a diseased larva is dissected, the midgut is opaque and milky white in appearance, as compared to the green midgut of an uninfected larva, and as the disease progresses the whitish appearance moves forward from the posterior end. The milky appearance of the midgut is due to the presence of huge numbers of polyhedra, present mainly in the cytoplasm of the epithelial cells. The cytoplasmic regions of the cells swell to some extent as the polyhedra are formed, and usually push into the lumen. Eventually, the cell membrane breaks and the polyhedral inclusion bodies are released into the lumen and then voided with the feces. Fecal contamination of mulberry leaves is an important source of infection in the farmer's rearing rooms.

The virions of CPV are enclosed in a crystalline protein matrix that has the overall shape of a polyhedron and may be as large as 1.5 μm across. The protein molecules are in simple cubic packing within this crystal; the array is disturbed only locally in the vicinity of an occluded virion. Three major strains of the virus have been distinguished on the basis of the shape of the polyhedron. One strain is called the "tetragonal" because the polyhedron has a tetragonal appearance in the light microscope. Electron micrographs of such forms, double-shadowed before observation, have demonstrated that the three-dimensional shape of this polyhedron is actually that of a cube. Another strain, called the "hexagonal," is distinguished by the fact that the polyhedra appear hexagonal in outline in the light microscope. There is fairly good evidence that the three-dimensional shape of these bodies is that of an icosahedron. The third strain, known as "pyramidal," has polyhedra which frequently appear triangular in outline. The three-dimensional shape is in question, but it may be that of a square pyramid with the square base and the four triangular facets slightly convex in contour. The morphology of the virions of the three major strains of CPV is apparently identical. Purification of the virus particles is achieved by dissolving the polyhedra in dilute alkali, thereby releasing their viral contents.

In the electron micrograph of Plate XV the CPV particles are about 65 nm in diameter and probably are composed of two concentric icosahedral shells. According to one proposed model each shell has twelve subunits, localized at the vertices of the icosahedron, with twelve tubular structures connecting the corresponding subunits of each shell. It is interesting to note that CPV has quite close similarity to reovirus and wound tumor virus, the former a virus of mammals, and the latter a virus of plants and insects. All three viruses have genomes consisting of double-stranded RNA, and all three contain a polymerase capable, *in vitro,* of transcribing this RNA to virus-specific, single-stranded RNA. As in the case of reovirus and wound tumor virus, the genome of

59

CPV appears, after isolation, to be in segments, nine of them with a total molecular weight of 12.7×10^6 daltons. Investigators have recently been active in the study of the physical relationship between the RNA subunits inside the structurally intact virus particle and in the RNA polymerase activity.

Selected Bibliography

Aizawa, K.: Structure of polyhedra and virus particles of the cytoplasmic polyhedrosis. In Aruga, H., and Tanada, Y. (Eds.) : *The Cytoplasmic-Polyhedrosis Virus of the Silkworm,* Tokyo, University of Tokyo Press, 1971, pp. 23–36.

Hukuhara, T.: Variations in cytoplasmic-polyhedrosis virus. In Aruga, H., and Tanada, Y. (Eds.) : *The Cytoplasmic-Polyhedrosis Virus of the Silkworm,* Tokyo, U of Tokyo Pr, 1971, pp. 61–78.

Ishimori, N.: Contribution a l'etude de la grasserie du ver a soie (Bombyx mori). *Compt Rend Soc Biol, 116:* 1169, 1934.

Kalmakoff, J., Lewandowski, L. J., and Black, D. R.: Comparison of the ribonucleic acid subunits of reovirus, cytoplasmic polyhedrosis virus, and wound tumor virus. *J Virol, 4:* 851, 1969.

Lewandowski, L. J., Kalmakoff, J., and Tanada, Y.: Characterization of a ribonucleic acid polymerase activity associated with purified cytoplasmic polyhedrosis virus of the silkworm *Bombyx mori. J Virol, 4:* 857, 1969.

Lewandowski, L. J., and Millward, S.: Characterization of the genome of cytoplasmic polyhedrosis virus. *J Virol, 7:* 434, 1971.

PLATE XVI

ROUS SARCOMA VIRUS

x 220,000

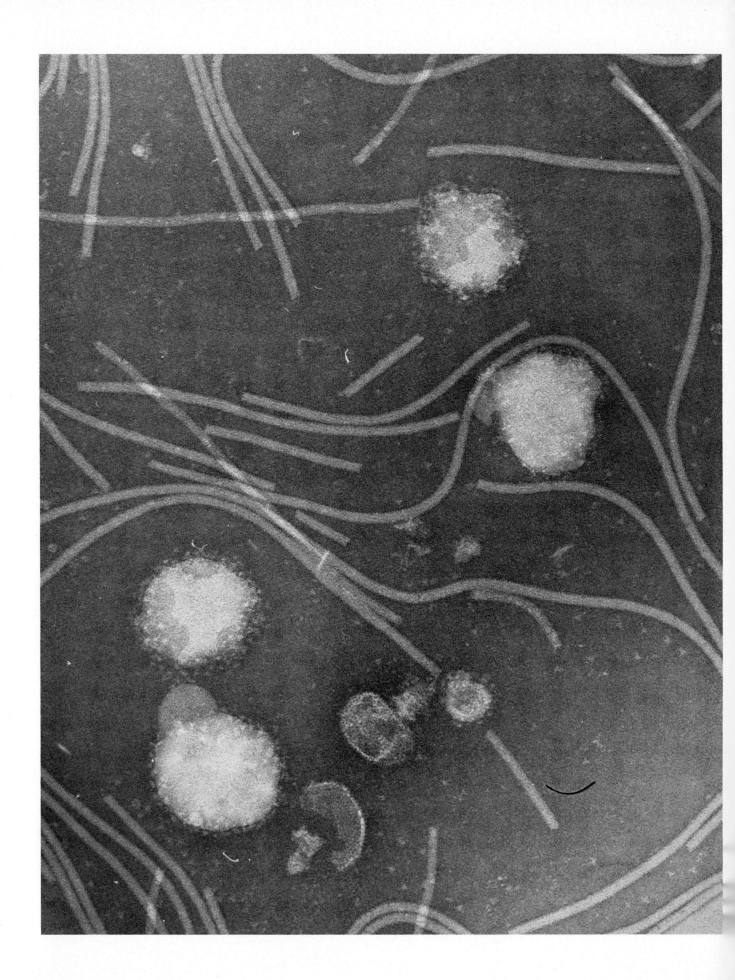

PLATE XVI   ROUS SARCOMA VIRUS   x 220,000

RNA, single-stranded, 1–2 percent

Isometric (pleomorphic?), enveloped, 80 nm

THERE ARE THREE GROUPS of animal viruses that are known to contain RNA and to be oncogenic: the mammary tumor virus, the murine leukemia viruses, and the avian leukosis and sarcoma viruses. A name proposed for all the viruses with these two characteristics is "oncornaviruses." The virus now known as Rous sarcoma virus (RSV) was first isolated by Peyton Rous in 1911, an accomplishment that closely followed the first isolation of any tumor virus, by Ellerman and Bang, in 1908. Avian tumor viruses, in general, may cause either leukemias or sarcomas in susceptible chicks. Rous sarcoma virus is laboratory transmitted by inoculation into the wing tissue where it almost invariably produces tumors if the chick is quite young, preferably one day old. The virus has been continued in laboratory passage ever since 1911, first in chick-to-chick transmittal, but more recently in tissue culture. In the intervening 62 years its characteristics may have changed many times, except for the selected trait, tumorogenicity, and there is no way to know whether or not the virus of the original isolate any longer exists. Several strains of RSV are now identified and used experimentally, with the Bryan strain being the one that is currently the most used.

When very young chicks are inoculated with RSV a certain proportion of them will develop solid tumors which usually metastasize. The incidence of such tumors is dependent upon dose, as well as upon factors intrinsic to the host animal, and this dose response can be used as a means of virus assay. More quantitatively precise assays are accomplished by inoculating chick fibroblasts in culture and scoring the effects by observation of the cells in the culture. The RSV is not cytocidal; rather, its effect upon cells is to *transform* them: to cause them to round up and to lose their normal inhibition against sliding over one another in crowded

cultures. As a result, a microscopic *focus* is formed in the vicinity of a cell that has been infected, the focus consisting of cells that have been secondarily infected with virus released from the initially infected one. These cells pile up on one another, owing to their loss of contact inhibition, and form a microscopic "tumor." The transformed cells continue to divide and seem to be in good health, despite their usual constant production of virus.

The oncornaviruses are extremely difficult to purify, and RSV is no exception. Since their lipid content is 20 to 30 percent, their density is low and is like that of lipid-containing cell membranes. This circumstance detracts enormously from the usually efficacious methods of density-gradient centrifugation. There is really no way to know at the present time whether anyone has made a preparation that is essentially pure. Electron microscopy exhibits particles of many sizes and shapes, some of which may be membrane vesicles, but others may be RSV particles of irregular outline. Despite the problems of purification the chemical nature of RSV is fairly well understood. Its RNA is single-stranded, and in undegraded form it has an S-rate of about 70, corresponding to a molecular weight of 10 to 12×10^6 daltons. It degrades to a 35S size under very mild denaturing conditions. The proteins of the RSV virion are not well characterized, but they are known to contain two virus-specific antigens. Antibodies to one of the antigens will neutralize all strains of RSV; it is therefore called group-specific. Antibodies to the other will specifically neutralize virus of the same strain, and the antigen is called strain-specific. The group-specific antigen is believed to be a protein located inside the virion, possibly on a nucleocapsid structure. Since the strain-specific antigen is found associated only with intact virus particles, as distinct from the group-specific antigen, it is believed to be part of the viral envelope. Other proteins known to exist in RSV are polymerases, of which there is discussion below.

Ribonucleic acid tumor viruses, including RSV, have a mode of information transfer that seems to be unique to them. The infecting virion contains not only its RNA but also an RNA-dependent DNA polymerase. After penetration and uncoating of the virion, the polymerase synthesizes a DNA provirus under the direction of the infecting RNA. This provirus remains in the infected cell and divides in synchrony with cell division. After some protein synthesis takes place the RNA of the progeny viruses is made, coded for by the provirus DNA; since the latter is always present, the cell can continue to produce virus particles. It would seem, then, that the DNA provirus has at least two functions: to code for new viral RNA and to modify the cell's genome in a manner so as to induce and perpetuate the transformed state.

Electron microscopy of the RNA tumor viruses has not yielded much structural information. As seen in sections, the virions can be classified into two groups: those that have a dense, central nucleoid and a smooth outer membrane (C-type particles), and those with an eccentric nucleoid and a membrane with regular projections (B-type particles). Nothing is known of the significance of these morphological distinctions. Sections of infected cells show that the maturing virions are extruded through the plasma membrane and seem to receive their membrane component by a budding process. The virions of partially purified RSV, as seen in negative stain, are quite

pleomorphic, but this appearance probably results from partial damage of the virion structure by the purification steps. Indeed, when the virions are seen clustered around the cell border, in preparations where the extruded virus is left *in situ* on the electron microscope film, the virions appear uniform in size and shape. Plate XVI shows some purified RSV particles that have apparently been little damaged; the only interesting feature is the existence of a fringe of triangular-shaped projections. Their significance is wholly unknown. Some work with other RNA tumor viruses, including avian myeloblastosis virus and murine leukemia virus, has suggested that the nucleoid of the virion contains a nucleocapsid helical structure that is regularly coiled into a tight ball.

Selected Bibliography

Robinson, W. S., and Duesberg, P. H.: The chemistry of the RNA tumor viruses. In Fraenkel-Conrat, H. (Ed.): *Molecular Basis of Virology.* New York, Reinhold, 1968, pp. 306–331.

Sarkar, N. H., Nowinski, R. C., and Moore, D. H.: Helical nucleocapsid structure of the oncogenic ribonucleic acid viruses (oncornaviruses). *J Virol, 8:* 564, 1971.

Temin, H. M.: Mechanism of cell transformation by RNA tumor viruses. *Annu Rev Microbiol, 25:* 609, 1971.

Temin, H. M.: The RNA tumor viruses—background and foreground. *Proc Natl Acad Sci USA, 69:* 1016, 1972.

Temin, H. M., and Rubin, H.: Characteristics of an assay for Rous sarcoma virus and Rous sarcoma cells in tissue culture. *Virology, 6:* 669, 1958.

Vogt, P. K., and Rubin, H.: The cytology of Rous sarcoma virus infection. *Cold Spring Harbor Symp Quant Biol, 27:* 395, 1962.

PLATE XVII

SINDBIS VIRUS

x 250,000

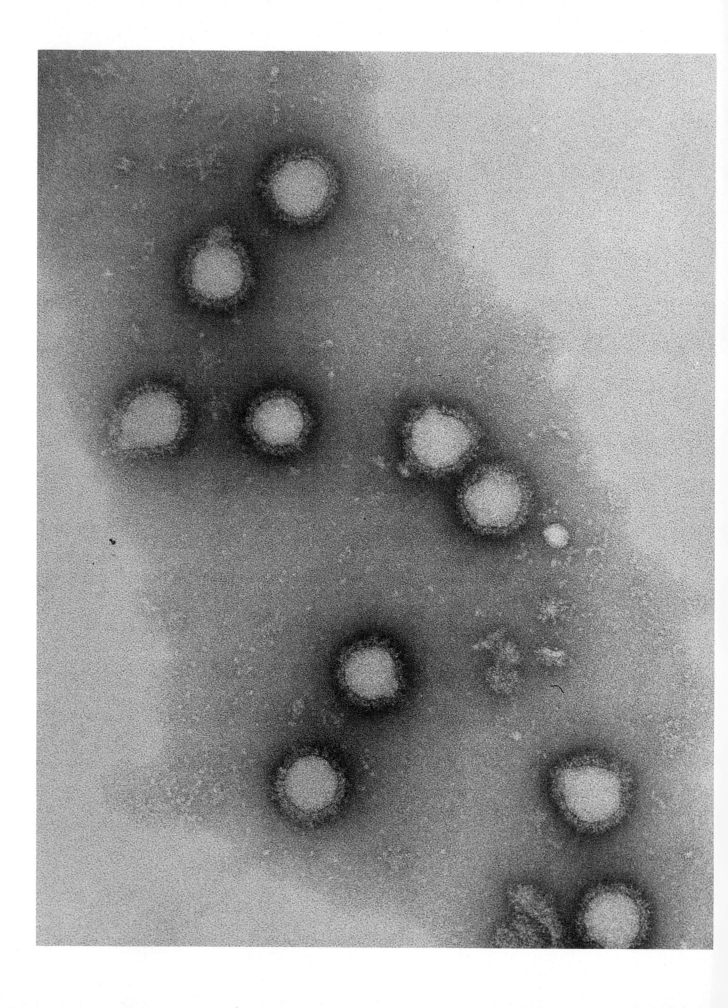

PLATE XVII   SINDBIS VIRUS   x 250,000

RNA, single-stranded, 6 percent

Isometric, enveloped and fringed, 60–70 nm, icosahedral nucleocapsid 35 nm

SINDBIS VIRUS is an arthropod-transmitted virus first isolated in 1952 from *Culex univittatus* mosquitoes in the Sindbis health district in the Nile Delta. The results of limited immunity surveys indicated that the virus was rather widely distributed in the Nile Valley and that it had a wide host range, including humans, domestic animals and avian species. Sindbis virus is fatal when injected into infant mice and embryonated eggs, and is markedly cytopathogenic to outgrowths of chick fibroblastic cells. It causes no known human disease. It is classed in group A arboviruses along with Western, Eastern, and Venezuelan equine encephalitis viruses because it can be grown in cultured cells more easily than the members of group B arboviruses such as yellow fever, St. Louis encephalitis, and Japanese encephalitis. All of the approximately 200 members of these groups are antigenically related, but distinguishable, and all are spherical, enveloped riboviruses containing single-stranded RNA.

The Sindbis virions seen on Plate XVII appear as spherical particles about 60 to 70 nm in diameter. They have an envelope which is covered with surface projections. Horzinek and Mussgay found conditions which would release the lipoprotein coat of this enveloped virus while leaving the nucleocapsid core intact. Such a result was achieved by treatment with 0.2 percent sodium desoxycholate and separation of the components by centrifugation in a sucrose gradient. The hemagglutinating activity of the membrane structures was recovered from the top fractions of the gradient and a nonhemagglutinating particle from the lower fractions. The particles in the latter fraction had a sedimentation coefficient of only 140S, contrasted with 273S for the intact virion. The cores appeared as spherical particles of 35 nm diameter, when examined as a negatively stained preparation in the electron microscope,

and they showed ring-like morphological units 12 to 14 nm in diameter on their surfaces. By correlating these images with the icosahedral classes of Caspar and Klug, the nucleocapsid structure was deduced to have the $T = 3$ arrangement, with hexamer-pentamer clustering, to yield 32 morphological units. Viruses with the architecture of Sindbis virus have been called "togaviruses," and fill the class of enveloped RNA viruses that have cubic symmetry in their nucleocapsids.

Sindbis virions apparently have one major protein in the nucleocapsid core and one major protein in the glycolipoprotein envelope. The ratio of protein:lipid:RNA is 66:28:6 and the molecular weight of the RNA is 2×10^6 daltons. Morphogenesis has been examined biochemically and by electron microscopy and appears to involve three distinct steps: (1) assembly of the nucleocapsid, (2) association of this core with the cell membrane, and (3) budding and release of the virions enclosed in a double-layered membrane. The membrane protein has been shown to be specified by the virus genome whereas the phospholipids and carbohydrate are derived from the host cell during the maturation and budding. Even though the carbohydrate moiety is covalently bound to virus-specified proteins, it apparently may be specified principally by the host. An electron microscopic study of the fusion of the cell membrane at the base of the budding virion in specimens prepared by freeze-etching techniques indicates that it is a two-step process; the inner leaflet fusing into a sphere before the outer one, and then followed by release of the virion into the medium.

Sindbis virus has been very useful in studies of *interferon* for several reasons. Not only can the virus be grown easily and quickly in chick fibroblast cultures, but it also induces dramatic production of interferon which inhibits the virus growth. It is generally accepted that in interferon-treated cells there is no synthesis of viral RNA, but there is no interference with the normal steps of attachment and uncoating. It is also generally understood that interferon stimulates cellular production of a protein which results in a virus-refractory state. Through study of the interaction of Sindbis virus RNA with ribosomes from normal and interferon-treated cells in a cell-free system, results have been obtained that indicate that the induced protein is a translation-inhibitory protein. This protein apparently functions by binding to ribosomes and inhibiting translation of the Sindbis viral RNA while permitting readout of normal cellular messenger RNA.

The ability of Sindbis virus to grow in either a vertebrate or arthropod host has undoubtedly exerted some selective pressure for growth over a broader temperature range than other viruses that can grow only in vertebrates. For this reason, Burge and Pfefferkorn considered Sindbis virus ideal for genetic studies with temperature-sensitive (ts), conditional lethal mutants and proceeded to isolate 23 ts mutants. They found these mutants were in two groups according to their ability to synthesize viral RNA at the restrictive temperature (40°C): 16 could not effect such synthesis (RNA−) and 7 could (RNA+), at rates between one-quarter and three-quarters the normal wild type rate. Genetic analysis of the RNA+ mutants placed them into three complementation groups which could be analyzed for their maturation defects by temperature-shift experiments. From these experiments they found that at 40°C the RNA+ mutants of one complementation group made defective viral core protein, another group of mutants apparently synthesize defective viral membrane protein (hemagglutinin), and of the third complementation group only one mutant, ts 20, was found. The ts 20 mutant apparently makes normal core and membrane, but not infectious virus, leading them to suggest that there is another viral protein required for maturation. All of the RNA− mutants are probably defective at 40°C in the production of RNA-polymerase proteins.

Selected Bibliography

Bose, H. R., and Sagik, B. P.: Immunological activity associated with the nucleocapsid and envelope components of an arbovirus. *J Virol, 5:* 410, 1970.

Brown, D. T., Waite, M. R. F., and Pfefferkorn, E. R.: Morphology and morphogenesis of Sindbis virus as seen with freeze-etching techniques. *J Virol, 10:* 524, 1972.

Burge, B. W., and Pfefferkorn, E. R.: Functional defects of temperature-sensitive mutants of Sindbis virus. *J Mol Biol, 35:* 193, 1968.

Horzinek, M., and Mussgay, M.: Studies on the nucleocapsid structure of a group A arbovirus. *J Virol, 4:* 514, 1969.

Marcus, P. I., and Salb, J. M.: Molecular basis of interferon action: Inhibition of viral RNA translation. *Virology, 30:* 502, 1966.

Simpson, R. W., and Hauser, R. E.: Basic structure of group A arbovirus strains Middelburg, Sindbis, and Semliki Forest examined by negative staining. *Virology, 34:* 358, 1968.

Taylor, R. M., Hurlbut, H. S., Work, T. H., Kingston, J. R., and Frothingham, T. E.: Sindbis virus: A newly recognized arthropod-transmitted virus. *Am J Trop Med Hyg, 4:* 844, 1955.

PLATE XVIII

BACTERIOPHAGE fd

x 440,000

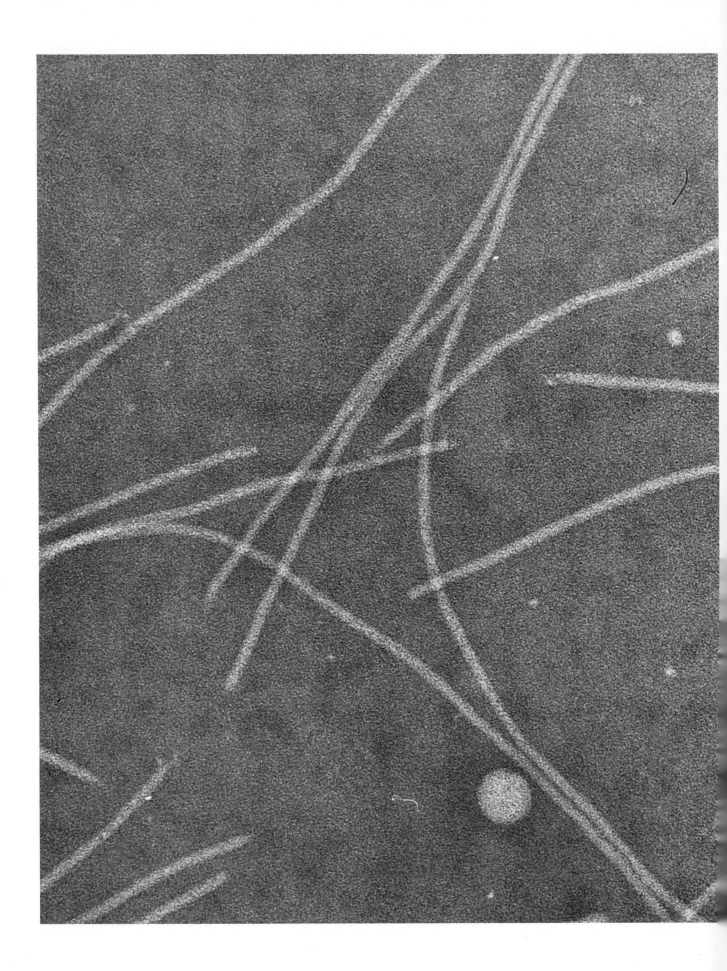

PLATE XVIII   BACTERIOPHAGE fd   x 440,000

DNA, single-stranded, 12 percent

Flexuous rod, *ca.* 850 nm × 6 nm, one end tapered

WHILE THE CLASSICAL bacteriophage particle is tadpole-shaped, with a DNA-containing head and an attached tail, in recent years two classes of bacteriophage particles with distinctly different morphological appearance have been found. One class consists of small, spherical virions which may contain (besides protein) either single-stranded RNA or DNA. The virions of the other class are nucleoproteins with a filamentous shape and containing single-stranded DNA (ss-DNA). One member of this class is called bacteriophage fd, illustrated in Plate XVIII.

The fd phage particle is about 850 nm long and only about 6.0 nm in diameter. It appears in electron micrographs as a flexuous rod with no evidence of surface structure. There have been reports that it contains an axial groove, or channel, but electron micrographs do not usually show such a feature, if it indeed exists. An interesting morphological finding is that the virion has a certain polar character; as can be seen in plate XVIII one end of a virion may appear either blunt or pointed. Each intact particle has one blunt end and one pointed one. Observations on DNA purified from fd phage show that it exists as a continuous loop; its form in the intact virion must be like a loop of thread that has been stretched taut. Since its contour length is about 2 μm it is clear that the DNA must extend throughout the length of the virion. The protein of fd phage consists almost entirely of one species, the B-protein, with a molecular weight of only about 5,200 daltons. A quantitatively minor protein, the A-protein, seems to be present as only one molecule (molecular weight about 70,000 daltons) per virion. It is very likely that the conical structure, about 10 nm long, seen at the tip of the pointed tail is the A-protein molecule, since its observed dimensions are in accord with those of a protein molecule of 70,000 molecular weight.

Virions of fd phage attach to the F pili of male strains of *Escherichia coli*. The attachment has been shown by electron microscopy to be end-to-end, as distinct from the attachment of the spherical RNA phages which is at the side of the pilus. While proof is lacking, it is tempting to conclude that the pointed tip of the fd phage (the A-protein?) is its attachment organ. Attachment is irreversible, and is followed by some kind of action which transports the entire virion to the bacterial interior. Whether the mechanism is one of conduction of the virion through a hollow tube in the pilus, or is mediated by a retraction of the pilus into the bacterium, is not firmly settled, but the evidence favors the latter view.

Infection by phages of the fd type is distinguished by the development of numerous progeny particles and by the nonlytic effect upon the host cell. Indeed, a resident infection seems to affect a bacterial culture in its growth characteristics only by a lowering of the growth rate. The production of virus is prodigious; a liter of culture may produce as much as 100 mg of purified virions. Upon entry of a virion into the cell it is uncoated and its ss-DNA is replicated (as it is with phage $\emptyset$X174) to form a double-stranded replicative form (RF). Further replication takes place to make many copies of RF, but it is not known whether only the initial RF complex may replicate (linear replication) or whether each new RF duplex may replicate (exponential replication). About 10 minutes subsequent to infection the accumulation of viral ss-DNA begins, as well as the extrusion of completed virions; these increase logarithmically in numbers until about 90 minutes post-infection at which time a steady state of viral production sets in. There is no accumulation of B-protein in the bacterial cytoplasm, suggesting that it may be stored in the membrane and become attached to viral DNA as the latter is extruded. Since no intact virions are found within infected cells, it must be that extrusion takes place rapidly once the joining of DNA and protein has been accomplished.

Inasmuch as the genome of the fd phage contains only about 6,500 nucleotides, enough to code for only 5 to 10 proteins of typical size, it should be possible to establish the number of genes within the virion and to determine something about their function. Complementation tests have identified eight genes in fd, although there may be some undiscovered ones. Four of them have identifiable functions: replication of RF and of infectious ss-DNA, and production of the A-protein and of the B-protein. With the exception of gene 2 (controlling RF replication) all known mutations cause cell killing under nonpermissive conditions. Infection by double mutants, one of which is defective in gene 2, does not cause cell killing. This observation suggests that gene 2 starts some cellular process such that, unless the whole phage production cycle is completed, the accumulation of the gene products will lethally interfere with normal cell physiology. Recombination experiments show the production of about 1 percent phenotypic recombinants: diploid virions of double length containing two separate genomes of normal length.

Selected Bibliography

Frank, H., and Day, L. A.: Electron microscopic observations on fd bacteriophage, its alkali denaturation products and its DNA. *Virology, 42:* 144, 1970.

Loeb, T.: Isolation of a bacteriophage specific for the F+ and Hfr mating types of *Escherichia coli* K-12. *Science, 131:* 932, 1960.

Marvin, D. A., and Hohn, B.: Filamentous bacterial viruses. *Bacteriol Rev, 33:* 172, 1969.

Smilowitz, H., Lodish, H., and Robbins, P. W.: Synthesis of the major bacteriophage fl coat protein. *J Virol, 7:* 776, 1971.

Wiseman, R. L., Dunker, A. K., and Marvin, D. A.: Filamentous bacterial viruses. III. Physical and chemical characterization of the Ifl virion. *Virology, 48:* 230, 1972.

Zinder, N. D., Valentine, R. C., Roger, M., and Stoeckenius, W.: fl, a rod-shaped male-specific bacteriophage that contains DNA. *Virology, 20:* 638, 1963.

PLATE XIX

VACCINIA VIRUS

x160,000

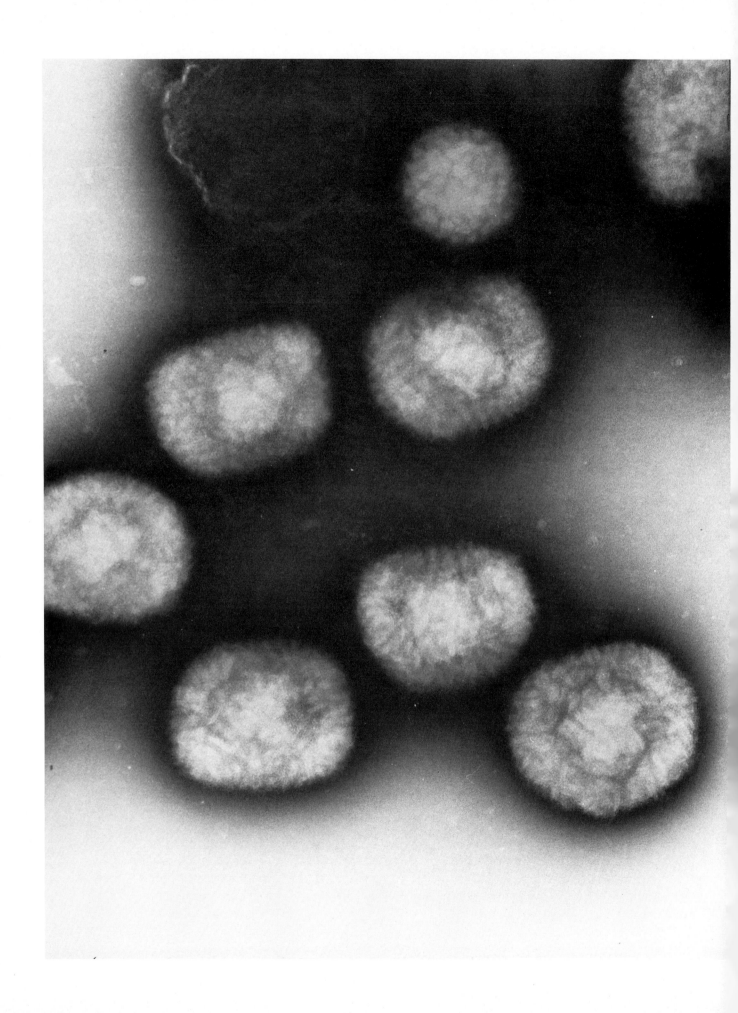

PLATE XIX   VACCINIA VIRUS   x160,000

DNA, double-stranded, 5 percent

Cuboidal, 200 nm × 200 nm × 300 nm

A PRIMARY PLACE of importance must be given to vaccinia virus for its role in conquering a dreaded disease and in effectively initiating the sciences of virology and immunology. It will be recalled that in 1796 Edward Jenner dramatically introduced vaccination against smallpox (variola virus), a widespread and deadly pestilence. After being cultivated artificially for so long, the present vaccinia virus probably has some differences from the original cowpox used by Jenner for vaccination. In addition to cowpox, the pox viruses are now known to be prevalent in a large variety of hosts such as fowl, sheep, swine and rabbits.

For about a century the agent of the disease in the pustules of vaccinated individuals was transmitted without identification. Because vaccinia is one of the largest animal viruses it was recognized as the "elementary bodies" seen at the limit of resolution of the light microscope as long ago as 30 years before the development of the electron microscope. The complexity of the structure and the large size of the brick-shaped vaccinia virus are seen in Plate XIX. Although the size and shape depend somewhat on the method of preparation, the particles have dimensions of about 300 × 200 × 200 nm. The virions have a clearly recognizable, dense central structure known as the core, or nucleoid, which can be dissociated from the virus by treatment with nonionic detergent and trypsin. This core contains the viral genome in the form of several broad cylindrical elements and is surrounded by an outer envelope. Within the virion are also two lateral bodies, one on each side of the core; this entire structure is enclosed in the outer membrane. The complex structure of vaccinia virus and its large size cause it to present different morphologies in different samples prepared for electron microscopy. Hence, there has been more than a little confusion in the description of the structure.

Because vaccinia virions are large and are available in large quantities, their general chemical composition was known long before that of other animal viruses. The virus contains about 90 percent protein, 5 percent DNA, and 5 percent lipid. The molecular weight of the double-stranded DNA has been estimated to be about 18×10^6 daltons from electron microscope measurements of its length as spread in protein monofilms. Contour measurements indicate that it is probably in one piece about 9 μm long. Although RNA has been reported to be present at the lower limit of chemical detection, special tests of the sensitivity of infectivity to the action of nucleases indicate that there is no RNA within the virion. The lipid material of the virion consists of cholesterol, phospholipid and neutral fat. This lipid is not part of an envelope derived from cell membranes, nor is it found in cores obtained by degradation with detergent. There are 17 or 18 proteins discernible in gel electrophoresis and gel diffusion tests of extracts of vaccinia-infected cells; however, only about seven have been identified as structural proteins of the purified virions when tested in immuno-diffusion with antiserum.

Vaccinia is one of the few DNA-containing viruses for which the whole process of multiplication takes place in the cytoplasm rather than partially in the nucleus of the host cell. This circumstance has allowed extensive investigation to be made, particularly in the electron microscope, of the initiation of infection, the biosynthetic events during the eclipse period, and the final maturation. Each infectious vaccinia particle forms a site of multiplication in the cytoplasm, called the viroplasm, or "factory," in which both DNA and protein synthesis take place. The one-step growth curve of vaccinia in cultured mammalian cells is only about ten hours, a comparatively short cycle. Studies on the sequence of events during growth have

75

revealed: (1) attachment to the cell membrane (mouse L cells) may be through any one of many sites all over the cell, (2) penetration is by engulfment and uncoating to release the core into the cytoplasm, an activity requiring about 20 minutes, (3) a second stage of uncoating, lasting about an hour, releases the viral DNA from the core, (4) viral messenger RNA is transcribed from the DNA by an RNA polymerase carried with the virion, (5) synthesis of viral DNA and protein takes place in the factory over the next three-hour period, and (6) condensation of DNA, assembly, and maturation take four more hours before release of the mature particles.

Selected Bibliography

Dales, S., and Siminovitch, L.: The development of vaccinia virus in Earle's strain L cells as examined by electron microscopy. *J Biophys Biochem Cytol, 10:* 475, 1961.

Easterbrook, K. B.: Controlled degradation of vaccinia virions *in vitro:* an electron microscopic study. *J Ultrastruct Res, 14:* 484, 1966.

Fenner, F., and Burnet, F. M.: A short description of the poxvirus group (vaccinia and related viruses). *Virology, 4:* 305, 1957.

Joklik, W. K.: The poxviruses. *Bacteriol Rev, 30:* 33, 1966.

Smadel, J. E., and Hoagland, C. L.: Elementary bodies of vaccinia. *Bacteriol Rev, 6:* 79, 1942.

Woodson, B.: Recent progress in poxvirus research. *Bacteriol Rev, 32:* 127, 1968.

PLATE XX

BACTERIOPHAGE ΦX174

x 400,000

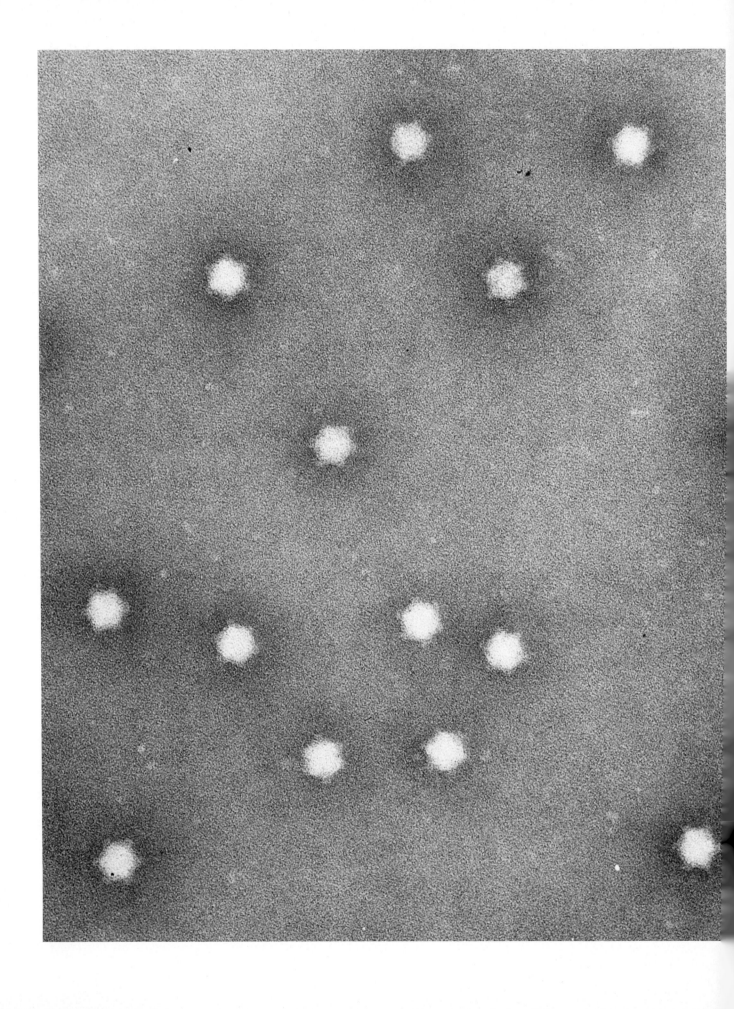

PLATE XX   BACTERIOPHAGE ΦX174   x 400,000

DNA, single-stranded, 25 percent

Isometric (icosahedral), spiked, 25 nm

Bacteriophage ΦX174, and its related phage S13, was discovered as long ago as 1935, but its physical and chemical properties were not investigated until 1959. These first studies showed that the virion was spherical and tailless, that it was only about 25 nm in diameter, and that it contained DNA. Later work, both by sedimentation analysis and electron microscopy, has shown that the DNA is single-stranded and circular, and that its molecular weight is only 1.7×10^6 daltons.

The virion of ΦX174 has an array of morphological subunits which strongly imply a T = 1 icosahedral structure. Thus, it should have 60 identical structural units. As seen in negative stain (Plate XX) the virion shows six spikes, an appearance to be expected if the virions are oriented on the substrate film with vertically directed 3-fold axes, and if there are a total of 12 spikes located on the 5-fold axes.

Four proteins have been isolated from ΦX174 virions. The most abundant is the capsid protein, with a molecular weight of 48,000 daltons. Sixty copies of this are found per virion, making it appear most likely that the 48,000 molecular-weight protein is the structural subunit. The three minor, lower molecular-weight proteins are identified as substructures of the 12 spikes of the icosahedral virion. Two of them are made in 60 copies each, while the third has but 12 copies. A reasonable structural model would show two 5-membered rings, consisting of the first two protein molecules, arranged concentrically with the axes of 5-fold symmetry through the spikes. Each spike would also have one copy of the fourth protein, although the insertion of this would perturb the icosahedral symmetry of the virion. There is general consensus, based upon infectivity studies of DNA-containing, spikeless mutants, and upon electron microscopy, that the organ of attachment of ΦX174 is any one of its

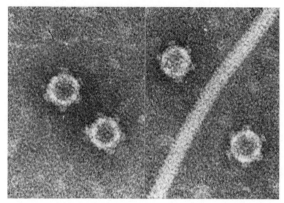

Figure 14. Empty phage ΦX174 particles, showing the spike structures. These are probably the attachment organs of the phage. ×320,000.

12 spikes. They appear relatively prominently in empty particles, as is seen in Figure 14. Since the protein of the virion does not enter the host cell following attachment, it is likely that the phage DNA is extruded along the axis of a spike.

The DNA of ΦX174 has a molecular weight of 1.7×10^6 daltons, enough to code for about ten ordinary proteins. Some eight genes have been found by genetic analysis, of which four code for the capsid and spike proteins, one codes for a lytic enzyme, and three code for DNA replication. There is some evidence that there are no large gaps in the genetic map; i.e. the coding capacity of the phage DNA is almost all accounted for.

When ΦX174 infects its normal host, E. coli, its circular ss-DNA is changed to a circular double-stranded form (RF) of which the parental DNA is one of the strands. Since this conversion can occur in the presence of a large dose of chloramphenicol (which blocks bacterial protein synthesis) it is likely that the enzyme(s) effecting the conversion is already in the uninfected cell. The replication of RF is continued until about 20 copies per cell are made. About 15 minutes post-infection, three changes occur: cell DNA synthesis stops, further net synthesis of RF ceases, and the synthesis of ss-DNA begins abruptly. Two genes are known to control ss-DNA function, and one controls RF replication. The ss-DNA is evidently packaged rapidly into intact virions since it is not found in free form in the host cell cytoplasm; intracellular φX174 particles containing ss-DNA are found abundantly after 10 to 15 minutes post-infection. The synthesis of ss-DNA and of three of the phage proteins is somehow interrelated, as evidenced by the fact that in cells infected with mutants defective in protein synthesis there is no accumulation of ss-DNA in the cytoplasm. In other words, if the DNA cannot be packaged it is not made, at least in stabilized form. ΦX174 is a lytic phage and infected cells burst to release phage progeny about 20 to 30 minutes after they are infected.

ΦX174 DNA has been used in a remarkable demonstration of the degree to which *in vitro* copying and synthesizing systems operate without error. The starting template was the phage's normal DNA. By use of a synthesizing system containing a DNA polymerase, a "joining enzyme," and the four deoxyribonucleoside triphosphates it was possible to convert the original ss-DNA to RF circles. The strand complementary to the starting DNA was separated from the parent strand (density labeling allowed this) and used as template for further synthesis. Replicated form duplex rings were again formed, the parent in these rings being the complementary strand. Once again the two strands of the duplex were separated. The strand complementary to the complementary strand, i.e. the one whose structure would be identical with the starting φX174 DNA if all went well, was tested for infectivity on spheroplasts. It was found to have a specific infectivity comparable to the DNA of the original φX174 virions. This work, accomplished in 1967, was the first instance of the synthetic production (with the aid of enzymes) of a nucleic acid, based on a template with biological specificity, with a sufficiently error-free nucleotide sequence to endow it with the same biological specificity as the natural template.

Selected Bibliography

Benbow, R. M., Hutchison, C. A. III, Fabricant, J. D., and Sinsheimer, R. L.: Genetic map of bacteriophage φX174. *J Virol, 7:* 549, 1971.

Burgess, A. B.: Studies on the proteins of φX174, II. The protein composition of the φX coat. *Proc Natl Acad Sci USA, 64:* 613, 1969.

Goulian, M., Kornberg, A., and Sinsheimer, R. L.: Enzymatic synthesis of DNA, XXIV. Synthesis of infectious phage φX174 DNA. *Proc Natl Acad Sci USA, 58:* 2321, 1967.

Ray, D. S.: The small DNA-containing bacteriophages. In Fraenkel-Conrat, H. (Ed.) : *Molecular Basis of Virology*, New York, Reinhold, 1968, Chapter 2, pp. 222–254.

Sinsheimer, R. L.: Purification and properties of bacteriophage φX174. *J Mol Biol, 1:* 37, 1959.

Sinsheimer, R. L.: A single-stranded deoxyribonucleic acid from bacteriophage φX174. *J Mol Biol, 1:* 43, 1959.

Sinsheimer, R. L.: Bacteriophage φX174 and related viruses. *Prog Nucleic Acid Res Mol Biol, 8:* 115, 1968.

PLATE XXI

RABBIT PAPILLOMA VIRUS

x 250,000

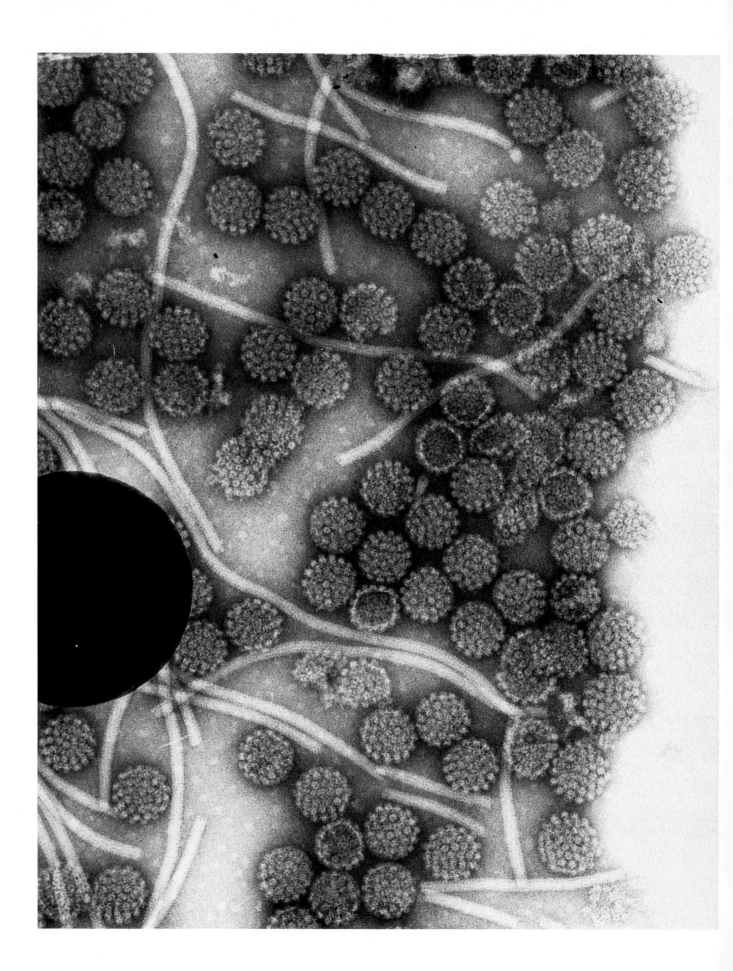

PLATE XXI   RABBIT PAPILLOMA VIRUS   x 250,000
(Shope Papilloma Virus)

DNA, double-stranded, 17 percent

Isometric (icosahedral), 55 nm

THE ISOLATION OF a virus from papillomatous lesions on the skin of wild cottontail rabbits was reported, by Shope, in 1933. Its isolation at first elicited no great interest among virologists, since the lesions were believed to be benign, but interest grew when it was later found that malignant tissue occasionally existed at the base of long-standing papillomas. It was also found that cell-free filtrates of ground papillomatous tissue could produce papillomas on the skin of domestic, as well as wild, rabbits after mechanical inoculation. Such lesions at first developed into benign tumors, but upon long standing they could become malignant. Thus, it could be claimed that the first isolation of a mammalian tumor virus had been accomplished, although an avian one, Rous sarcoma virus, had been known for many years.

A puzzling aspect of the early studies on the experimental transmissibility of the rabbit papilloma virus was the degree to which its quantity and infectious potential seemed to vary widely. If the wild rabbit was the experimental host in the first passage the virus was readily extractable from the tumors and was capable of successful transmission to a new host. But if the domestic rabbit was the host on first passage, little or no virus seemed to be produced, as measured by extractability and transmissibility. In this case, however, the donor tumors exhibited the presence of viral antigen, as shown by fluorescent-antibody tests, and could produce antigen-containing tumors if they were grafted to a new host. These findings led to a long-continued controversy about "masked" viruses: Viruses which were present in tissue as antigen, but which had no pathogenicity after isolation from the tissue. In 1956 Beard laid to rest the speculations about the masking of papilloma virus by inoculation tests with highly purified virus that could be precisely quantitated. He found that a truly enormous dose (something like 10^8 particles) was necessary to produce experimental tumors, and deduced convincingly that the failure of extracts of domestic rabbit tumors to be transmissible was due simply to their relatively low virus content.

Rabbit papilloma virus is one of a small group of viruses that cause skin tumors, generally benign. Other members of the group are the papilloma viruses of dogs and cattle, and the human papilloma, or wart, virus. The response of these viruses to growth in cell culture varies considerably. They rarely exhibit cytopathic effect, but those from cattle have a measurable potential for cell transformation, about 10^5 infectious units per cell transformed. The virus of rabbit papilloma causes no cytopathic nor transformation changes in those cell cultures that have been tested; hence, the titration of extracts containing the virus is still restricted to measuring tumor production on the skin of domestic rabbits.

The complete virions of rabbit papilloma virus (Plate XXI) are isometric and quite uniform in size. Purified extracts contain some empty particles (those devoid of nucleic acid) and some structural variants appearing like long, round-ended tubes with the same diameter as that of the normal virion. The DNA in the intact virus particle is easily released by treatment with phenol and is found to be in the form of double-stranded circles that are supercoiled. Supercoiling occurs when the number of turns in a DNA helix, in circular form, is either less or greater than that resulting from normal Watson-Crick base pairing. In Shope papilloma DNA the number is less than normal, as is shown by the fact that heating the DNA in formaldehyde, thereby allowing denatured regions to untwist, converts the circular molecule to an unsupercoiled form. Measurements by sedimentation velocity and electron microscopy agree in assigning to the DNA a molecular weight of 5×10^6 daltons. The molecular weight of the protein subunit of papilloma virus has not been thoroughly studied but is believed to be about 40,000 daltons.

The capsomeric arrangement of the virion of rabbit papilloma virus has been the subject of some controversy, but now is well settled. The capsomers are remarkably prominent, as Plate XXI shows. In fact, they were the first to be seen on any virus, in 1953, in micrographs of shadowed specimens. Their number was such that it suggested either a T = 4, or a T = 9, icosahedral surface lattice, if only the P = 1 or P = 3 series were considered (see Introduction). But Finch and Klug noted in 1965 that the capsomeric array, as seen in projection when both the upper and lower surfaces of the virion are contrasted with negative stain, showed prominent "beaches" and "eyes" (visible in Plate XXI). From this observation they entertained the notion, novel at the time, that the virion was built on a *skew* lattice in which T = 7. Since this arrangement would have 72 morphological units (capsomers) they built a model of this kind and compared their projected images, at various orientations, with their electron micrographs. They found that the beaches and eyes could be found in the projections of the model. In a few cases they observed in their micrographs particles that had been contrasted on only one surface, and in these the arrangement of five-coordinated and six-coordinated capsomers was that expected of a T = 7 array. Later work, in which stereo electron microscopy and computer-generated virus models were employed, confirmed the early conclusion that the rabbit papilloma virus had 72 capsomers, on a T = 7 icosahedral surface lattice, and the skewness was *laevo*. The same kind of arrangement was found for the human wart virus, except that it is *dextro*. So far, these are the only viruses known with a skewed capsomeric structure.

Selected Bibliography

Beard, J. W.: The fallacy of the concept of virus masking: A review. *Cancer Res, 16:* 279, 1956.

Finch, J. T., and Klug, A.: The structure of viruses of the papilloma-polyoma type. III. Structure of rabbit papilloma virus. *J Mol Biol, 13:* 1, 1965.

Ito, Y.: A tumor-producing factor extracted by phenol from papillomatous tissue (Shope) of cottontail rabbits. *Virology, 12:* 596, 1960.

Kleinschmidt, A. K., Kass, S. J., Williams, R. C., and Knight, C. A.: Cyclic DNA of Shope papilloma virus. *J Mol Biol, 13:* 749, 1965.

Klug, A., and Finch, J. T.: Structure of viruses of the papilloma-polyoma type. IV. Analysis of tilting experiments in the electron microscope. *J Mol Biol, 31:* 1, 1968.

Shope, R. E.: Infectious papillomatosis of rabbits. *J Exp Med, 58:* 607, 1933.

PLATE XXII

SIMIAN VIRUS 40

x 320,000

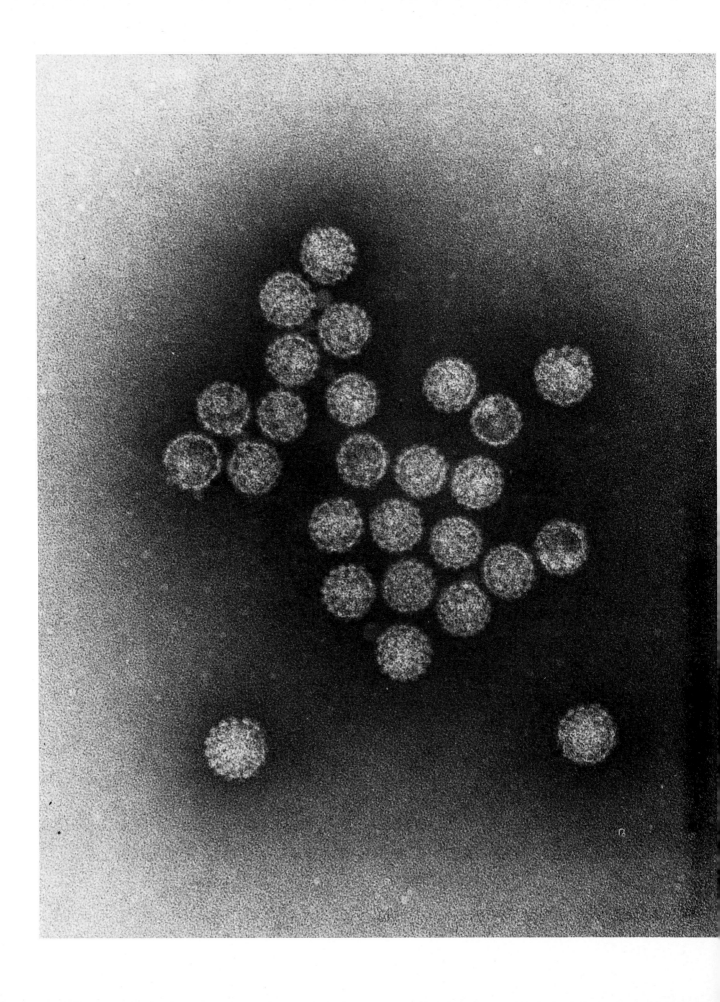

PLATE XXII   SIMIAN VIRUS 40   x320,000

DNA, double-stranded, 12 percent

Isometric (icosahedral), 45 nm

VIRUSES OF SIMIAN tissues gained special interest from the time that monkey kidney cell cultures were commonly used in the preparation of virus vaccines for human use. As a result of the extensive use of primate cell cultures a great number of new viruses were isolated as tissue contaminants and designated as "SV" (for simian virus), with serial numbers irrespective of their properties or taxonomic order. One of these viruses (which happened to be the fortieth discovered) was called the "vacuolating virus," because of the prominent cytoplasmic vacuolation found in infected cell cultures, and was given the designation SV 40. It appeared to be a ubiquitous contaminant of monkey kidney cell cultures, and initially was demonstrated to be present in all three types of Sabin's live poliovirus vaccines, thereby raising the question of the safety of administration to infants. Interest in the contaminating virus turned to concern when evidence was presented to show that an oncogenic virus in extracts of rhesus monkey kidney cells, responsible for the production of tumors in hamsters, was SV 40.

Of all the simian viruses, SV 40 is by far the most intensively studied, and is generally grouped with other small, nonenveloped, icosahedral deoxyriboviruses which replicate in the nuclei of vertebrate cells. The widely used name for this group of viruses is papovavirus ("pa" from papilloma, "po" from polyoma, and "va" from vacuolating agent). There are small differences in the size of the virions in the group (those of papilloma are larger than polyoma or SV 40), but the close similarity can be seen by comparing the SV 40 virions shown on Plate XXII with those of papilloma shown on Plate XXI. Essentially all of the viruses in the papovavirus group have been shown to cause solid tumors in a large variety of hosts.

Of the deoxyriboviruses SV 40 is one of the smallest animal viruses with a diameter of only about 45 nm. The double-stranded viral DNA has a molecular weight of only 3×10^6 daltons, making up about 12 percent of the particle weight. This means that there is only enough genetic information to code for six to eight small proteins. Analyses by electrophoresis in polyacrylamide gels containing sodium dodecyl sulfate of full and empty virions separated by isopycnic centrifugation have led to the conclusion that, since there are five different polypeptides, more than three fourths of the viral genome is used for coding the structural components. Two polypeptides of molecular weight 43,000 and 32,000 daltons comprise 80 percent of the protein of the virus capsid. Three other polypeptides of much lower molecular weight form an internal nucleoprotein in the virion.

According to electron microscopic and sedimentation analyses, when the SV 40 DNA is free of the capsid it is found in several different conformations. One form is a twisted, circular molecule which can be converted to an open circle by a single break in one strand, or to a linear form by a break in both strands. The problem of replication of such a double-stranded circular nucleic acid has been considered with the aid of several alternative models. An earlier model, originally proposed for bacteriophage lambda, was called the rolling-circle model. However, later findings for the replicative intermediates (RI) of SV 40 seemed to favor a swivel model. Two types of replicating DNA molecules were observed in preparations from infected cultures: (1) an open structure containing two branch points, three branches and no free ends, and (2) a similar structure with all the same features which also contained a superhelix in the unreplicated portion of the molecule. Eighty to 90 percent of the RI were in the latter configuration indicating that most of the replicating molecules do not have a swivel point in the unreplicated region. This finding poses some conceptual problems on the unwinding of the parental duplex, since such unwinding would necessarily produce twists until it became impossible to unwind the covalently bonded parent molecule. This difficulty was resolved by proposing an *intermittent swivel* in the unreplicated portion. The simplest kind of swivel could be produced by the introduction of a single-strand break. An intermittent swivel could be provided for by an endonuclease that would produce single-strand breaks and a sealing ligase which would repair the break after the supercoiled condition had been relaxed. Polynucleotide ligase activity has been described in cells infected with SV 40. The exact relationship, in time and space, of the growing point with the nicking and sealing is still open for investigation.

In addition to the cytocidal replication of SV 40 DNA, it is also possible for the DNA to interact with some cells in a way which alters, rather than destroys, the cell. Under appropriate conditions a tumor virus such as SV 40 may cause cells to: (1) grow in an uncontrolled fashion, (2) change their response to contact with one another, (3) become a permanent culture (able to multiply without limit), (4) acquire new antigens (see adenovirus, Plate XXIV), (5) acquire an unstable and altered karyotype, (6) change appearance and differentiated characteristics, and (7) change metabolic patterns with an increased acid production. Some of these induced changes of growth and contact response of cells cultured *in vitro* have stimulated so much investigation that there is concern that, to some, cancer might be considered a disease of the petri dish. Of the many cell alterations the most controversial have been those referred to as "contact inhibition of movement" and "density-dependent in-

hibition of replication." Cells from normal tissues, when in culture, cease movement and growth when they are unable to escape contact from one another, whereas after transformation with a tumor virus this inhibition is lost. The direct conceptual link between cell movement and replication has not been made, although it has been shown that in colony growth from a single cell replication ceases as soon as the cells cannot escape one another; only the peripheral cells then multiply. Also, untransformed cells are unable to multiply in agar suspension where there is no substrate that permits migration away from each other. Cell growth regulation through a surface-mediated mechanism, and the loss of this control by a virus transformation, is an interesting problem in cell biology.

Selected Bibliography

Bourgaux, P., Bourgaux-Ramoisy, D., and Dulbecco, R.: The replication of the ring-shaped DNA of polyoma virus, I. Identification of the replicative intermediate. *Proc Natl Acad Sci USA, 64:* 701, 1969.

Dulbecco, R.: Cell transformation by viruses. *Science, 166:* 962, 1969.

Eddy, B. E., Borman, G. S., Grubbs, G. E., and Young, R. D.: Identification of the oncogenic substance in rhesus monkey kidney cell cultures as simian virus 40. *Virology, 17:* 65, 1962.

Fisher, H. W., and Yeh, J.: Contact inhibition in colony formation. *Science, 155:* 581, 1967.

Ozer, H. L., and Tegtmeyer, P.: Synthesis and assembly of simian virus 40. II. Synthesis of the major capsid protein and its incorporation into viral particles. *J Virol, 9:* 52, 1972.

Sebring, E. D., Kelly, T. J., Jr., Thoren, M. M., and Salzman, N. P.: Structure of replicating simian virus 40 deoxyribonucleic acid molecules. *J Virol, 8:* 478, 1971.

Sweet, B. H., and Hilleman, M. R.: The vacuolating virus, S.V.40. *Proc Soc Exp Biol Med, 105:* 420, 1960.

Todaro, G. J., and Green, H.: High frequency of SV40 transformation of mouse cell line 3T3. *Virology, 28:* 756, 1966.

PLATE XXIII

CAULIFLOWER MOSAIC VIRUS

x 360,000

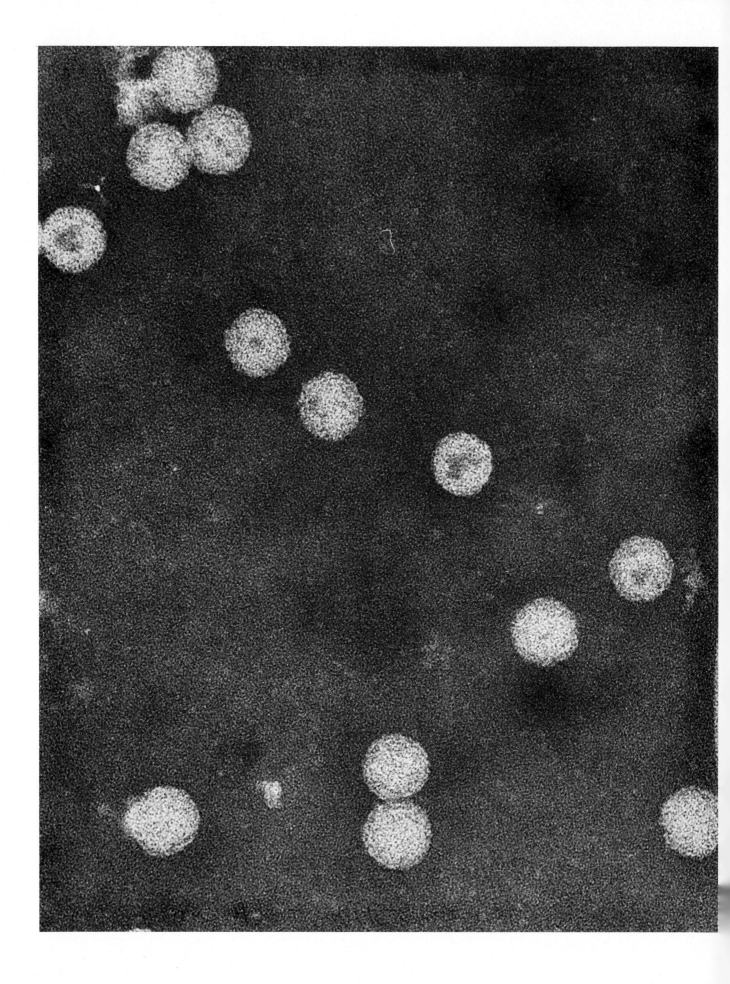

PLATE XXIII   CAULIFLOWER MOSAIC VIRUS   x360,000

DNA, double-stranded, 15 percent

Isometric, 50 nm

THE CAULIFLOWER mosaic virus (CAMV) causes a systemic disease in cauliflower plants and in related species such as mustard. The visible sign of the disease is a decoloration and banding of the leaf veins, accompanied by some stunting of the growth of the plant. The natural transmission of the virus is by aphids, but successful transmission can be effected by mechanical inoculation. Although the virus was first isolated and purified as long ago as 1960, it attracted no particular attention until 1968. In that year Shepherd, Wakeman and Romanko made the surprising discovery that the nucleic acid of the virus was DNA. Until that time one of the tenets of virology was that plant viruses contained only RNA, either single- or double-stranded.

The virions of CAMV have no remarkable structure to go along with their remarkable nucleic acid. They are spherical, about 50 nm in diameter, and have so far shown no electron microscopically observable substructure (Plate XXIII). The protein subunits of the capsid have a molecular weight somewhat over 30,000 daltons. In contrast to turnip yellow mosaic virus and the group of viruses that include brome mosaic, the DNA of CAMV is evidently tightly bound in the virion. It can be quantitatively extracted only after treatment with pro-

nase or papain; even these enzymes are less effective alone than when used sequentially with sodium dodecyl sulfate (SDS). Recent work has extended the original characterization of the DNA. Its sharp thermal melting point, and its adenine/thymine and cytosine/guanine ratios of unity, indicate that it is double-stranded. Electron micrographs of DNA that has been released as gently as possible from the virions, and observed immediately after isolation, show a great preponderance of circular forms, with a contour length indicating a molecular weight of 4.6×10^6 daltons. There is some evidence from analysis of nearest-neighbor frequency of bases that the DNA has the same design as that of the host cell, a situation encountered in some of the small viruses of animals.

Selected Bibliography

Day, M. F., and Venables, D. G.: Purification of cauliflower mosaic virus. *Virology, 11:* 502, 1960.

Russell, G. J., Follett, E. A. C., and Subak-Sharpe, J. H.: The double-stranded DNA of cauliflower mosaic virus. *J Gen Virol, 11:* 129, 1971.

Shepherd, R. J., Bruening, G. E., and Wakeman, R. J.: Double-stranded DNA from cauliflower mosaic virus. *Virology, 41:* 339, 1970.

Shepherd, R. J., Wakeman, R. J., and Romanko, R. R.: DNA in cauliflower mosaic virus. *Virology, 36:* 150, 1968.

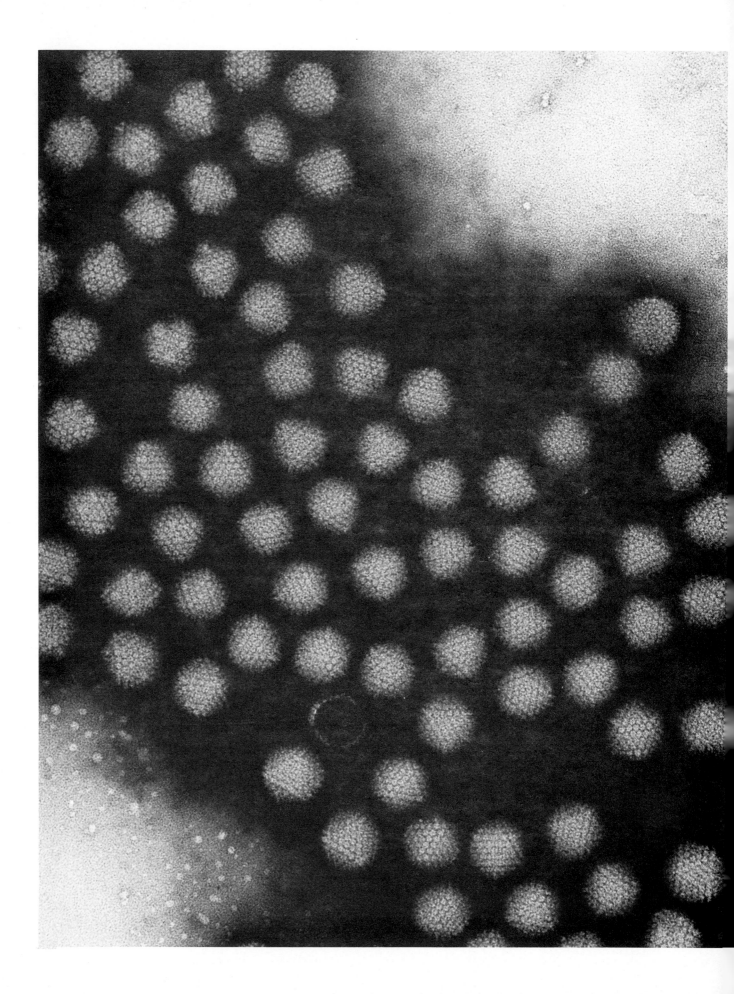

PLATE XXIV   ADENOVIRUS   x 210,000

DNA, double-stranded, 13 percent

Isometric (icosahedral), 72 nm

I N THE EARLY 1950's human adenoids and fore-
skin were two of the few noncancerous
human tissues available for starting *in vitro*
cell cultures. The adenoid tissues, available
from operations on young children, repeatedly
showed a characteristic degeneration when
they were established in tissue culture. From
the supernatant fluid of the degenerating cultures a filterable cytopathogenic agent was
found, one that proved to be serially transmissible to other established tissue cultures
such as HeLa. It was tentatively proposed
to designate this agent as the "adenoid degen-
erative agent." Eventually, isolation and identification established that the agent was indeed
a rather picturesque virus and that there were
about 30 different but related human adenoviruses which cause sore throats and respiratory
diseases in children. There are similar adenoviruses which infect dogs, monkeys, chickens,
and other hosts.

Adenoviruses are relatively large and give
an impressive demonstration of the capsomeric
detail on an icosahedron, as is seen in Plate
XXIV. The virion is about 72 nm in diameter
and has a distinct hexagonal close-packed arrangement of capsomers on the surface. Each
of the 20 sides has six capsomers along each
edge of its equilateral triangular face; such
an arrangement results in a total of 252 capsomers in the whole virion. The 12 capsomers
at the vertices of the icosahedron are different
from those on the faces in that they have
"antennae" which extend radially about 10 nm
from the virion surface (Figure 15).

The terminology proposed for the components of the capsid of adenovirus is *hexon* for
the nonvertex capsomers and *penton* for the
ones at the icosahedral vertices. Each of the
former is surrounded by six other capsomers
(hence its name), while each of the pentons,
carrying the fiber projections, is surrounded

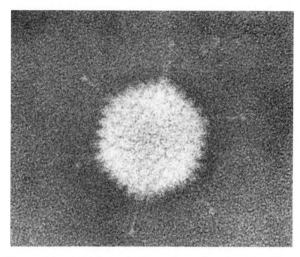

Figure 15. A virion of adenovirus, showing the fibers
that extend from the pentons. ×390,000.

by five capsomers. The hexon capsomer has
a molecular weight of 360,000 daltons, composed of three copies of a single type of polypeptide subunit of molecular weight 120,000.
The basic unit of the penton capsomer, serologically distinct from the hexon, is composed
of three subunits of a single type of peptide
of molecular weight 70,000 daltons. During
virus growth the pentons and hexons are both
synthesized in excess and can be purified from
infected cells. In fact, the hexons represent
one of the rare virus capsomers which have
been purified and crystallized. The crystals
have a tetrahedral shape and a complete absence of birefringence, indicating that they have
a cubic space group. The fibrous appendage
on the penton can be removed by trypsin digestion and purified. It is found to consist of a
single fiber with a terminal knob, and to have
antigenic properties that are distinctive to it.
Since they protrude well beyond the surface of
the virion, the fibers with the terminal knobs
are suspected of having activity in adsorption
and hemagglutination.

Adenovirus was the first human virus shown

93

to induce tumors in hamsters. Newborn hamsters were injected subcutaneously between the shoulders with about 5×10^6 plaque-forming units of adenovirus and were found about one month later to have very large tumors. Once the tumor had been induced the virus could no longer be recovered from it. The 31 different serotypes of human adenovirus can be divided into groups of highly oncogenic, weakly oncogenic, and nononcogenic on the basis of this kind of test in hamsters. Since the adenovirus also can be grown in large quantity in tissue culture, and its DNA isolated in a highly purified form, it is possible to correlate the degree of oncogenicity with the composition of the DNA in terms of (1) the percent of the total weight of the virion, (2) the percent guanine plus cytosine (G + C), and (3). the homology of the viral DNA to other viruses as determined by hybridization tests. The highly oncogenic group is found to have the lowest DNA content and the lowest G + C content. The various members within each group are closely related, as shown by 80 to 85 percent DNA-DNA homology between their DNA's, but they share little (10 to 20 percent) base sequences with members of the other groups.

The DNA of adenovirus appears to be linear and double-stranded, with a molecular weight between 2.1 and 2.3×10^7 daltons and comprising 11 to 14 percent of the particle weight. When the internal core, which contains the viral DNA, is released by treatment of the virion with 5M urea the DNA is found to be in association with three arginine-rich polypeptides of molecular weight 44,000, 24,000 and 24,000 daltons. These peptides comprise about 20 percent of the total viral protein and are not found in the empty capsids that may be isolated as upper components after crude virus preparations are subjected to cesium chloride gradient centrifugation. One of these empty capsids is seen in Plate XXIV.

In addition to possessing the three structural antigens (hexons, pentons and fibers) synthesized in virulent infections the oncogenic adenoviruses and other tumor viruses, like SV 40 (see Plate XXII), cause the synthesis of two new kinds of antigens in the tumor cells. These new antigens are not part of the virion but are induced by it, and hence have been referred to as "footprints" of a tumor virus. One of these induced specific antigens found in tumor, or transformed, cells is called the tumor, or "T," antigen. It is localized in the nucleus where it can be detected by the complement-fixation reaction, by fluorescent antibody, and by ferritin-tagged antibody used in electron microscopy. Since the T antigen appears very shortly after inoculation by the virus it has been suggested that it may be one of the early enzymes induced by viruses; however, thymidine kinase and several other known enzymes have been ruled out by direct test. The other newly formed antigen found in adenovirus-induced tumors and in transformed cells is called the transplantation antigen. It is considered to be a virus-specific surface antigen. Animals can be protected against tumor formation by one kind of virus by immunizing injections with that virus but they remain susceptible to tumor formation upon challenge with a different virus of the oncogenic group.

Selected Bibliography

Ginsberg, H. S., Pereira, H. G., Valentine, R. C., and Wilcox, W. C.: A proposed terminology for the adenovirus antigens and virion morphological subunits. *Virology, 28:* 782, 1966.

Green, M.: Oncogenic viruses. *Annu Rev Biochem, 39:* 701, 1970.

Maizel, J. V., Jr., White, D. O., and Scharff, M. D.: The polypeptides of adenovirus. II. Soluble proteins, cores, top components and the structure of the virion. *Virology, 36:* 126, 1968.

Norrby, E.: The structural and functional diversity of adenovirus capsid components. *J Gen Virol, 5:* 221, 1969.

Pereira, H. G., Huebner, R. J., Ginsberg, H. S., and van der Veen, J.: A short description of the adenovirus group. *Virology, 20:* 613, 1963.

Rapp, F., and Melnick, J. L.: The footprints of tumor viruses. *Sci Am, 214:* 34, March 1966.

Schlesinger, R. W.: Adenoviruses: The nature of the virion and of controlling factors in productive or abortive infection and tumorigenesis. *Adv Virus Res, 14:* 1, 1969.

Valentine, R. C., and Pereira, H. G.: Antigens and structure of the adenovirus. *J Mol Biol, 13:* 13, 1965.

PLATE XXV

TIPULA IRIDESCENT VIRUS

x135,000

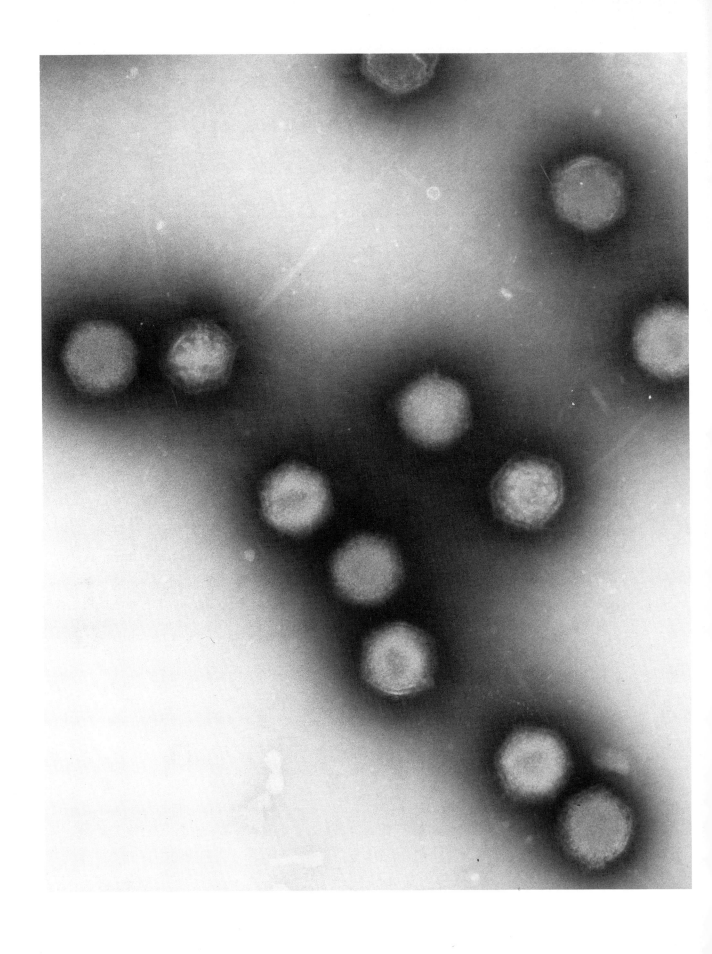

DNA, double-stranded, 19 percent

Isometric (polyhedral), 130 nm

INSECTS, particularly in the larval stage, are commonly found to harbor virus infections. Observations of insect tissues, combined with virus assay, have shown that the viruses may multiply in the nuclei of infected cells, or in the cytoplasm where they may exist either as free particles or as many virions encapsulated in a polyhedral protein matrix. The *Tipula* iridescent virus (TIV) which infects the crane-fly *Tipula paludosa* (its natural host) is the best characterized of the insect viruses that develop as free particles within the cytoplasm. In the laboratory it can be successfully inoculated only to larvae, wherein it grows to an astonishing degree in the cytoplasm of the fat-body cells. In late infection, just before the larva dies, the infection has spread throughout the body, causing it to take on an opalescent color. At this time the virus can easily be extracted and purified, as was first done in 1954. The amount of virus may be as much as 25 percent of the larva's dry weight, the record for any virus in any organism.

The origin of the unscientific adjective, iridescent, attached to the virus lies in the coloration of severely diseased larvae and in the magnificent array of color that is seen when a pellet of purified virus is examined by reflected white light. The pellet has the appearance of a brilliant opal (as indeed it should; opals consist of an array of spherules of about the size of TIV and packed much like the virus within a pellet). The virus pellet consists of a multitude of small crystals in random orientation. The large virions of TIV are spaced within the crystal such that the separation between crystal planes is comparable with the wave lengths of visible light. Thus, Bragg reflections will cause different colors to be strongly reflected, depending upon the spacing of the crystal planes involved, and the entire mass of crystallites will appear opalescent, or iridescent. Of the other known viruses only vaccinia would be large enough (>100 nm) to appear iridescent when packed in a pellet, but it is not sufficiently uniform in size and shape to pack into crystalline array.

The first sound evidence that a virus particle could have a polyhedral shape with sharp corners came in 1957 from examination of TIV. After the virions were frozen-dried to preserve external morphology, and double-shadowed from two angles 60° apart, the shadows cast were almost identical with that of an icosahedral model that was similarly "shadowed" with a flashlight (Figure 16 a and b). This finding was important in understanding the architecture of viruses; while it did not prove that TIV (and perhaps some other viruses) was built with icosahedral *symmetry*, it was consistent with the subsequent, and correct, proposals by Caspar and Klug that the shells of spherical viruses are actually constructed with this symmetry.

Tipula iridescent virus is a double-stranded DNA virus, whose virion consists of about 20 percent DNA and about 80 percent protein, with perhaps some phospholipid. Sections of pellets of the virus show particles with relatively electron opaque cores, suggesting that the denser

Figure 16. Demonstration of the icosahedral shape of the *Tipula* iridescent virus. (a) A model of an icosahedron "shadowed" at two angles 60° apart. (b) Electron micrograph of a frozen-dried virion shadowed at the same angles. Note close similarity of the shapes of the shadows.

DNA is centralized in location. Work with sections prepared so that those virus particles found as slices within them could be enzymatically digested confirms this intimation of the nature of the core. The outer portion of the virion can be removed by the action of pepsin, while the action of trypsin and DNAse will selectively remove the core. The latter finding implies that the core is not solely DNA, but rather that it is made up of fairly closely bound DNA and protein. Analysis of isolated cores (obtained after action of pepsin) shows them to contain about 35 percent DNA and 65 percent protein.

The TIV virion in intact form cannot productively be examined by electron microscopy for evidence of capsomeric arrangement. That it has a regular arrangement of protein subunits can hardly be doubted, in view of its icosahedral shape. Fortunately, but mysteriously, the virions can be partially degraded by the nasal decongestant commercially known as Afrin, to reveal capsomeric structure to some extent. Additionally, if the virus is stored for months in water at 4°C, organized portions of its capsid become dislodged and can be readily examined in the electron microscope. By use of these techniques of partial disaggregation Wrigley has been able to arrive at a likely capsomeric structure for TIV and for a morphologically similar virus (SIV) from *Sericesthis pruinosa*. It was concluded that the capsid of TIV contains 1,472 capsomers, or possibly 1,562, the number contained by SIV. The former corresponds to $T = 147$ in the Caspar-Klug scheme of virus structure, if the capsomers are clustered hexagonally and pentagonally (at the 12 vertices). Since the total number (S) of structural units, presumably identical protein molecules, must satisfy $S = 60\ T$, there would be 8,820 such molecules within the TIV capsid. The molecular weight of the protein subunits of TIV has been found to be close to 3×10^4 daltons. Hence, total protein mass represented by the observed capsomers is 2.5×10^8 daltons, only one-fourth the total protein in the virion (1×10^9 daltons). It is thus probable that TIV is more complex than its surface structure indicates, and that it contains more than one shell of capsid material.

Selected Bibliography

Kalmakoff, J., and Tremaine, J. H.: Physicochemical properties of *Tipula* iridescent virus. *J Virol, 2:* 738, 1968.

Thomas, R. S., and Williams, R. C.: Localization of DNA and protein in *Tipula* iridescent virus (TIV) by enzymatic digestion and electron microscopy. *J Biophys Biochem Cytol, 11:* 15, 1961.

Williams, R. C., and Smith, K. M.: A crystallizable insect virus. *Nature (Lond), 179:* 119, 1957.

Wrigley, N. G.: An electron microscope study of the structure of *Tipula* iridescent virus. *J Gen Virol, 6:* 169, 1970.

Xeros, N.: A second virus disease of the leatherjacket, *Tipula paludosa. Nature (Lond), 174:* 562, 1954.

PLATE XXVI

HERPES SIMPLEX VIRUS

x 200,000

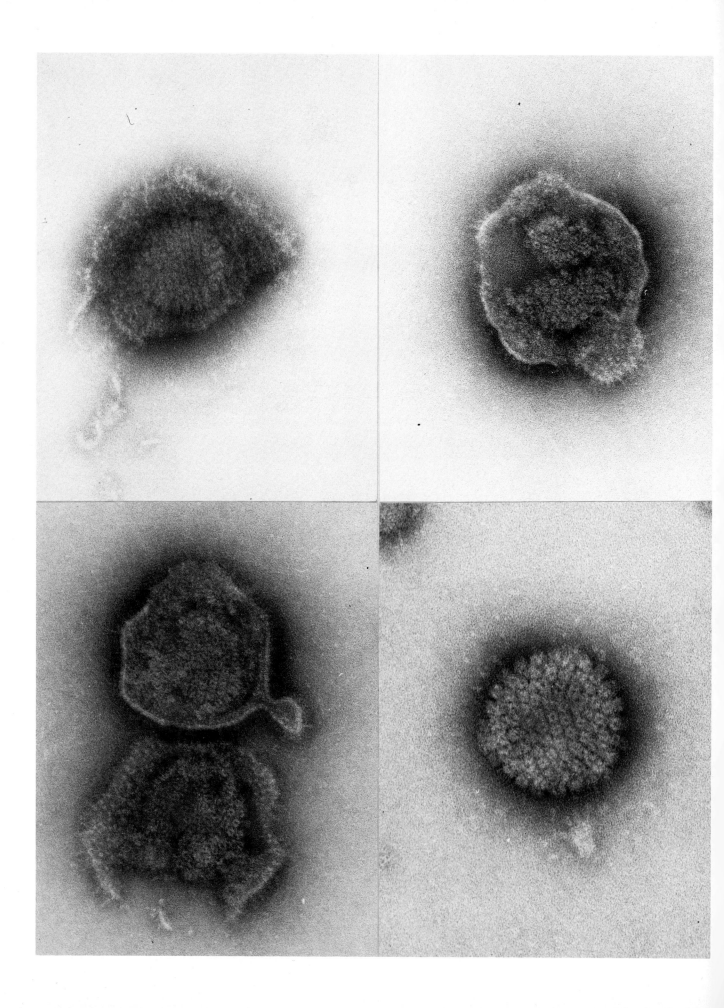

PLATE XXVI   HERPES SIMPLEX VIRUS   x 200,000

DNA, double-stranded, 7 percent

Isometric (icosahedral), enveloped and fringed, 180 nm

HERPES SIMPLEX is one of a group of deoxy-riboviruses which originally attracted attention because most adults in the population possess neutralizing antibodies against it in their blood. More recently the herpes viruses have become additionally interesting because of their involvement in oncogenesis. The name, herpes, is very old and has been used in medicine since the time of Hippocrates to describe certain kinds of diseases of the skin. The true nature of herpes simplex was questioned for some time because the virus did not appear to be an infectious agent that was transmitted from one victim to another, but seemed to be generated endogenously by individuals after nonspecific stimuli. Later it was recognized that the primary infection with herpes simplex is very common in infants, and, that after recovery, the virus disappears and goes into a quiescent, latent state from which it can be reactivated by various factors which cause the infection to recur even as an adult. External stimuli such as cold, wind, or ultraviolet irradiation, and physiological or emotional stresses can cause recurrence of the disease as cold sores and fever blisters.

Other members of the herpes virus group produce a variety of diseases in humans and animals. These include: (1) varicella and zoster, which are really different manifestations of the same virus in the form of chicken pox or shingles; (2) pseudo rabies, which has been called "mad itch" because of the vigorous rubbing which cattle do to their affected parts; and (3) equine abortion and bovine rhinotracheitis and many others. All these members of the herpes virus group are characterized uniquely not only by containing double-stranded DNA of about 10^8 daltons molecular weight and by the large size of their virions, but also by the presence of nuclear inclusions in cells infected by them.

The finding that the herpes viruses are etiologic agents in certain neoplasms of chickens, monkeys and frogs, along with some evidence that they may contribute to the genesis of human lymphomas, has radically changed our thinking about the importance of this virus, particularly in view of the widespread incidence of antibodies to it in the human population. One of these neoplasms, Marek's disease, is a highly contagious, malignant lymphomatosis in chickens that creates major economic problems for the poultry industry. This disease has been shown to be caused by a herpes virus that can be grown in chick or duck embryo fibroblasts in culture, where it produces cytopathogenic effects. It is interesting that the development of neoplastic disease by this virus is a rare event, in contrast to the high frequency with which the host cells are infected in a non-malignant, self-limiting form. A herpes virus has also been identified in the Lucké frog renal carcinoma, and herpes saimiri has been isolated from the lethal lymphatic leukemia and reticulum cell sarcoma of primates. A most notable development in the study of viral oncogenesis was the demonstration by electron microscopy of the Epstein-Barr virus, a previously unknown member of the herpes virus group, in cell cultures from Burkitt's lymphoma as well as in infectious mononucleosis. The Epstein-Barr virus is strongly suspected as a possible causative agent in human lymphomas.

Detailed electron microscopic studies of the herpes simplex virion by thin sectioning and negative staining have shown that its structure is not at all simple. This complexity is seen in the four different views shown in Plate XXVI. All of the evidence indicates that there is a central core surrounded by an inner membrane inside the capsid and an envelope surrounding it. The core, containing the DNA, has an average diameter of about 77 nm and discloses a polyhedral shape in thin sections. The nucleocapsid is about 105 nm in overall diameter and has an icosahedral symmetry. Since there are five capsomers on each edge of the icosahedral array the entire capsid must contain 162 capsomers. The capsomers appear like hollow, elongated, polygonal prisms with five or six sides. The prisms at the 12 vertices of the icosahedron seem to be pentagonal, whereas the six-sided ones make up the rest of the capsid. They measure 9.5 nm in diameter by 12.5 nm in length, and have an axial hole of 4.0 nm diameter.

The outer envelope has a laminated structure very similar to the cell membrane and has an overall diameter of 180 nm. Periodic projections similar to the spikes of myxoviruses are visible at its periphery. The exact composition of the envelope is not known, but the lipid and glycoproteins present suggest that the envelope is added as the capsid of the virion matures and passes through the cytoplasmic or nuclear membrane of the cell as it emerges. This suggestion is strengthened by the results of serological studies which show that the virion envelope contains antigenic material of host origin.

Selected Bibliography

Beswick, T. S. L.: The origin and the use of the word herpes. *Med Hist, 6:* 214, 1962.

Darlington, R. W., Granoff, A., and Breeze, D. C.: Viruses and renal carcinoma of *Rana pipiens*. II. Ultrastructural studies and sequential development of virus isolated from normal and tumor tissue. *Virology, 29:* 149, 1966.

Epstein, M. A., Henle, G., Achong, B. G., and Barr, Y. M.: Morphological and biological studies on a virus in cultured lymphoblasts from Burkitt's lymphoma. *J Exp Med, 121:* 761, 1965.

Kaplan, A. S.: *Herpes Simplex and Pseudorabies Viruses*. (Virology Monographs, 5) New York, Springer-Verlag, 1969, 115 pp.

Klein, G.: Herpesviruses and oncogenesis. *Proc Natl Acad Sci USA, 69:* 1056, 1972.

Nazerian, K., Solomon, J. J., Witter, R. L., and Burmester, B. R.: Studies on the etiology of Marek's disease. II. Finding of a herpesvirus in cell culture. *Proc Soc Exp Biol Med, 127:* 177, 1968.

Wildy, P., Russell, W. C., and Horne, R. W.: The morphology of herpes virus. *Virology, 12:* 204, 1960.

PLATE XXVII

BACTERIOPHAGE T4

x 450,000

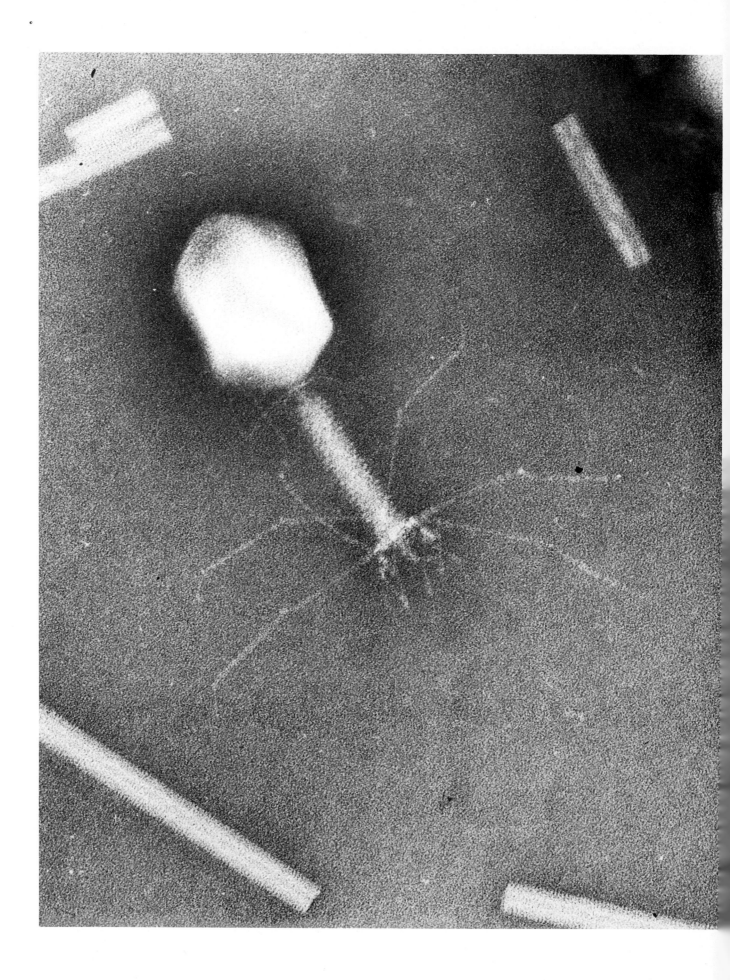

PLATE XXVII   BACTERIOPHAGE T4   x 450,000

DNA, double-stranded, 50 percent

Binal: prolate head 65 × 95 nm, rigid helical tail 20 × 95 nm, attached fibers

EVER SINCE THE EARLY 1940's the bacterio-phages that use *Escherichia coli* as host cell have been the favored research object of a number of investigators. In 1945 the seven strains of these phages were designated T1 through T7, and it was found soon thereafter that the even-numbered ones were closely related, both structurally and serologically. Cooperative and concentrated efforts were devoted toward investigating the T-even phages for several compelling reasons: (1) their host, *E. coli,* was easily and rapidly grown on simple media, both in suspension and on solid agar; (2) the T-even series provided an interchangeable source of information on the composition, life cycle, mechanism of infection and synthesis of virus-specific protein, RNA, and DNA; (3) they have a high efficiency of plating, short growth cycle, and large burst size; (4) quantitative electron microscopy had shown that one physical particle is one infective unit; and (5) the T-even system was very amenable to quantitative methods for purification and assay and for determination of genetic characteristics.

Even though chemical analysis showed that bacteriophage T4 was roughly half DNA and half protein, early electron microscopy illustrated how complex and intricate the structure was compared to the regular helical and isometric plant viruses (Plate XXVII). Early micrographs revealed that the viral DNA was enclosed in a head membrane which could be osmotically shocked to release the DNA, leaving behind the empty, broken head membrane with an attached tail. These head membranes were also found to be one of the intracellular virus components which appeared during the so-called *eclipse* period of phage development, an interval during which no infectious phage could be detected in a one-step growth experiment.

Several details of the structure of the DNA of the T-even phage have been puzzling. S. S. Cohen found that the hydrolysis products of the DNA did not give the normal nucleotide composition, but yielded a new base, 5'-hydroxymethylcytosine, where other DNA's have cytosine. In some way, as yet not fully understood, this base permits an unusual association of glucose residues with the nucleic acid, rendering it less susceptible to nucleases. The extreme fragility of the DNA polymer, which is easily broken by shearing during its isolation, prevented an early realization that the head actually contained only one piece (possibly circular) of DNA with a molecular weight of 130×10^6 daltons. The mechanism for packing this amount of DNA inside the head membrane still remains a mystery; however, the polyamines which are also found in the head may play a charge-neutralizing role.

Just as the DNA can be separated from the protein by osmotic shock, so is it also separated in some way during the earliest phase of the infective process. This fact was beautifully demonstrated in the famous blender experiment performed by Hershey and Chase. They used purified phage which had been radioactively labeled—the protein with an isotope of sulfur and the nucleic acid with an isotope of phosphorus. This phage was used to show that, after its attachment to the host cell, only the DNA entered the cell during the infection process. This knowledge gave a big boost to the idea of the primacy of DNA in heredity and in the capability of this polymeric molecule to store and transfer information. The first clue to the mechanism of the transfer of the information from DNA was provided by experiments of Volkin and Astrachan on T2 phage. They showed that shortly after infection a new, rapidly turning-over RNA appeared in the cells. The base composition of this RNA was different from normal *E. coli* DNA but was similar to the phage DNA. Although they suggested that the new RNA might be involved in phage-specific protein synthesis, it was several years before the messenger RNA hypothesis emerged.

As fascinating as these discoveries in the growth and structure of T-even phage were, they were surpassed by the outstanding contributions in the field of genetics. After 1946, when the first mutants for rapid lysis of the host cell (r mutants) were described, experiments rapidly demonstrated host range (h) mutants, geometric multiplication, recombination, and linkage. By 1955, Benzer had devised methods to: (1) carry out genetic complementation tests; (2) define the cistron as the functional genetic unit from the complementation, or *cis-trans,* test; (3) complete the fine structure mapping in which the size of the recombination unit was of the order of the intra-nucleotide distances on the viral DNA; and (4) prepare a complete topographic map of the rapid lysis (rII) region from over 300 distinct mutation sites. Unfortunately, it turned out to be very difficult to isolate the gene product of the rII gene and to account for the time of lysis, lysis inhibition, and the exact role of lysozyme. The discovery later of a large number of new kinds of mutants, particularly the conditional lethal mutants such as the so-called amber (am) and the temperature-sensitive (ts) ones, permitted the complete, circular genetic map eventually to be drawn and to be associated with the phage's physiological and morphological constituents. By utilizing subcellular *in vitro* systems the genetic link to phenotypic expression is emerging. For example, active lysozyme of phage T4 has been synthesized in a cell-free system programmed by RNA purified from infected cells.

The tail structure of the T-even phages, as shown by phage T4 in Plate XXVII, is exceedingly complex. There are at least seven morphologically distinct parts: (1) a thin, disc-shaped collar about 36 nm in diameter; (2) two extremely fine fibers attached to the collar; (3) a central tube with an interior hole only about 2.5 nm in diameter; (4) a contractile tail sheath covering the central tube which can shorten to

about 35 nm from its original 80 nm during the infection process; (5) a distal base plate with six points; (6) short fibers, or spikes, about 40 nm long attached to the base plate; and (7) six long tail fibers, about 130 nm long and bent in the middle, attached to the six points of the base plate. All of these parts seem to play a role in the attachment, adsorption, and penetration steps by which the T4 DNA is transferred into the host cell.

With this variety of head and tail parts the T-even bacteriophage have been a model for studying the morphogenesis of a complex virus. As mentioned above, it had been long established that at least the head membrane was made independently during the *eclipse* period. The gene products of the large number of conditional lethal mutants which were isolated later supplied a way to study the ordered sequence in the subassembly of the head and tail parts. This was done by accumulating the incomplete parts in a nonpermissive infection and examining them in the electron microscope as they were tested *in vitro* for complementation in the assembly of complete virions from the separate parts. The investigations established a morphogenetic pathway for the flow of the gene products into the completed virus particles. It has several notable features: (1) There are three independent assembly lines for forming the head, the tail, and the tail fibers; (2) the assembly of the tail starts with the base plate followed by the core and then the sheath; (3) the formation of the head has several steps in which the head capsomers are made and put together and the empty structure filled with DNA; (4) the completed heads and tails go together spontaneously; and (5) the long tail fibers, already assembled in their separate sequence, are attached to the base plate as the last step in the whole assembly process.

Selected Bibliography

Benzer, S.: Fine structure of a genetic region in bacteriophage. *Proc Natl Acad Sci USA, 41:* 344, 1955.

Benzer, S., Delbrück, M., Dulbecco, R., Hudson, W., Stent, G. S., Watson, J. D., Weidel, W., Weigle, J. J., and Wollman, E. L.: A syllabus on procedures, facts, and interpretations in phage. In Delbrück, M. (Ed.): *Viruses 1950.* Pasadena, California Institute of Technology, 1950, pp. 100–147.

Plate XXVII—Bacteriophage T4 107

Epstein, R. H., Bolle, A., Steinberg, C. M., Kellenberger, E., De La Tour, E. B., and Chevalley, R.: Physiological studies of conditional lethal mutants of bacteriophage T4D. *Cold Spring Harbor Symp Quant Biol, 28:* 375, 1963.

Hershey, A. D., and Chase, M.: Independent functions of viral protein and nucleic acid in growth of bacteriophage. *J Gen Physiol, 36:* 39, 1952.

Levinthal, C., and Fisher, H.W.: Maturation of phage and the evidence of phage precursors. *Cold Spring Harbor Symp Quant Biol, 18:* 29, 1953.

Luria, S. E., Williams, R. C., and Backus, R. C.: Electron micrographic counts of bacteriophage particles. *J Bacteriol, 61:* 179, 1951.

Salser, W., Gesteland, R. F., and Bolle, A.: *In vitro* synthesis of bacteriophage lysozyme. *Nature (Lond), 215:* 588, 1967.

Stent, G. S.: *Molecular Biology of Bacterial Viruses.* San Francisco, Freeman, 1963, 474 pp.

Volkin, E., and Astrachan, L.: Phosphorus incorporation in *Escherichia coli* ribonucleic acid after infection with bacteriophage T2. *Virology, 2:* 149, 1956.

Wood, W. B., and Edgar, R. S.: Building a bacterial virus. *Sci Am, 217:* 60, July 1967.

Wyatt, G. R., and Cohen, S. S.: The bases of the nucleic acids of some bacterial and animal viruses: the occurrence of 5-hydroxymethylcytosine. *Biochem J, 55:* 774, 1953.

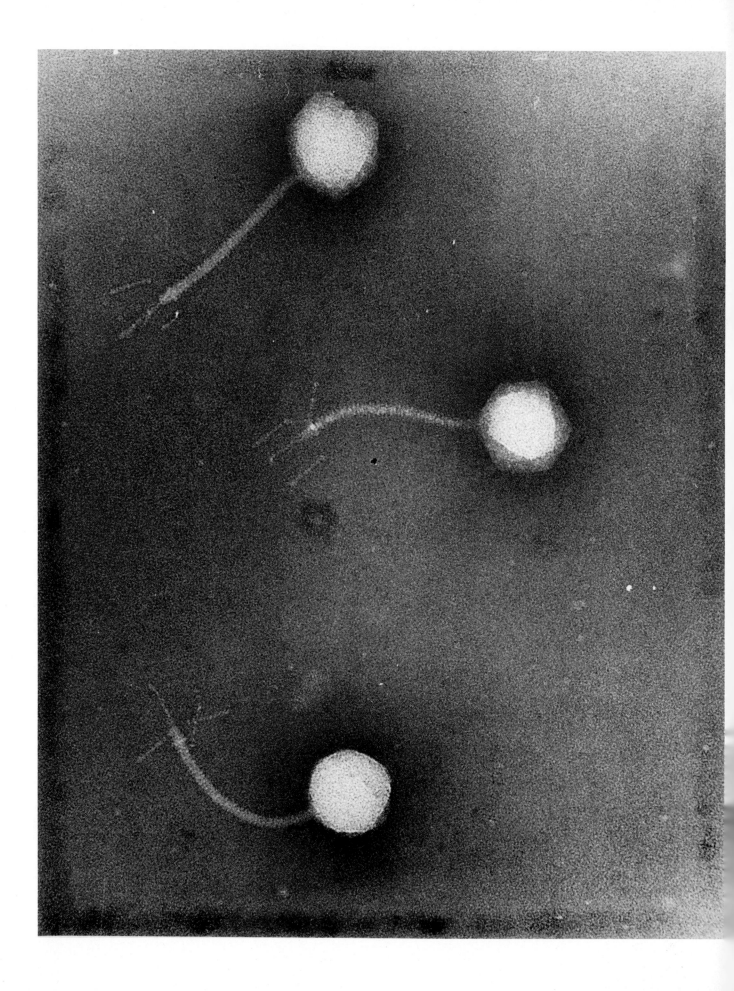

PLATE XXVIII   BACTERIOPHAGE T5   x270,000

DNA, double-stranded, 50 percent

Binal: isometric head (polyhedral) 90 nm, flexuous helical (?) tail 13 × 200 nm, attached fibers

IN ONE OF THE EARLIEST reviews of bacteriophages it was pointed out that four developments could be listed which played significant roles in the rapid advance of research on these viruses. These were (1) the systematic use of the technique of the *one-step growth experiment;* (2) the concentrated attention of the investigators on the same T-series of bacteriophages; (3) the proof that bacterial virus-resistant variants arise by spontaneous mutation; and (4) the application of the electron microscope to settle controversies in connection with the peculiar morphology of bacterial viruses. Bacteriophage T5 has played a significant role in at least two of these areas of advance, the early stages of the one-step growth experiment, and in the electron microscope studies.

When the artifacts resulting from the forces of surface tension were eliminated from the specimen preparation for electron microscopy, bacteriophage T5 was found to have a head which was hexagonal in contour. The tail is noncontractile, striated, and with dimensions of 200 × 13 nm. Some of the unique features of this attachment organ provided the tools for the study of the early parts of the one-step growth experiment. These early steps in the virus infection included attachment, adsorption, penetration, and injection.

The tail of bacteriophage T5 provided a system to study the receptor substance on the *E. coli* surface for the adsorption of the phage. Weidel and his colleagues were able to extract and purify this substance from the wall of the cell and to show that the *E. coli* cell wall is composed of three layers: an outer lipoprotein layer, a lipopolysaccharide component, and a rigid inner mucoprotein layer. Electron microscopy established that the T5 receptors were localized in the outer two layers. One particle of the purified receptor substance can combine with only one T5 particle *in vitro* and in the

process of combination exerts a specific inactivating effect on the bacteriophage by triggering ejection of the DNA from the T5 particle. Receptor particles from the T5-resistant mutant of *E. coli* called B/1,5 are identical morphologically with the wild type, but do not attach to T5 tails and do not inactivate the phages.

Another unusual and unique feature of bacteriophage T5 infection is that injection of the DNA into the cell takes place in two separable steps. This was discovered in 1960 by Y. T. Lanni who found only a small fraction of the DNA from the parental phage in the host cell after ten minutes. This first-step-transfer (FST) DNA, as it was called, was found to comprise about 8 percent of the molecular weight of the mature T5 DNA and was shown to be in specific fragments of uniform size. After a few minutes of protein synthesis by the cell it is receptive to the remaining 92 percent of the DNA from the infecting phage. This extends the latent period of bacteriophage T5 to 40 minutes, compared to the 13 to 25 minutes for the other phages in the T-series.

The discontinuous transfer of DNA during T5 infection has made possible a more detailed study of the sequence of the well-ordered events that are initiated by the infective process. It has also permitted researchers to determine which fragments of the infecting DNA control specific functions. At least three classes of proteins are formed under the direction of the T5 nucleic acid and these are grouped according to the period of time during which they are synthesized. Class I proteins appear between 0 and 6 minutes after infection, class II between 6 and 18 minutes, and class III from 14 minutes until lysis. The *in vitro* transcription of T5 DNA by use of purified RNA polymerase has shown that there are three corresponding temporal classes of T5-specific RNA. Hybridization techniques with this transcribed RNA and fractions of the phage DNA have demonstrated that the earliest RNA corresponds to the first-step-transfer DNA.

It appears that the class I proteins include those necessary to shut off host protein synthesis (thereby degrading the bacterial DNA), and another protein necessary to participate in the transfer of the second part of the phage DNA. Class II proteins include the early enzymes necessary for phage DNA metabolism such as thymidylate synthetase, deoxynucleotide kinase, and DNA polymerase. The class III proteins include those which make up the structural components of the head and tail.

As might be expected, interest in the anatomy of the T5 DNA molecule was stimulated by the two-step process in which it is transferred to the host cell. Sedimentation analysis and electron microscopy have led to models of the structure in which (1) there are interruptions in the polynucleotide chains of the molecule at specific, genetically determined points along its path; (2) the nucleotide sequence of the linear, double-stranded DNA is unique and not circularly permuted; (3) the FST DNA section is separated by a single-strand interruption which is a point of preferred breakage from the rest of the phage genome; and (4) the phage carries only one such section and therefore always transfers the asymmetrical DNA molecule of 7.5×10^7 daltons into the host cell in the same direction.

Selected Bibliography

Abelson, J., and Thomas, C. A., Jr.: The anatomy of the T5 bacteriophage DNA molecule. *J Mol Biol, 18:* 262, 1966.

Bujard, H.: Location of single-strand interruptions in the DNA of bacteriophage T5+. *Proc Natl Acad Sci USA, 62:* 1167, 1969.

Cohen, S. S.: *Virus-Induced Enzymes.* New York, Columbia U Pr, 1968, 315 pp.

Lanni, Y. T.: First-step-transfer deoxyribonucleic acid of bacteriophage T5. *Bacteriol Rev, 32:* 227, 1968.

Pispa, J. P., and Buchanan, J. M.: Synthesis of bacteriophage T5 specific RNA *in vitro. Biochim Biophys Acta, 247:* 181, 1971.

Weidel, W., and Kellenberger, E.: The *E. coli* B-receptor for the phage T5. II. Electron microscopic studies. *Biochim Biophys Acta, 17:* 1, 1955.

Williams, R. C., and Fraser, D.: Morphology of the seven T-bacteriophages. *J Bacteriol, 66:* 458, 1953.

PLATE XXIX

BACTERIOPHAGE T7

x 250,000

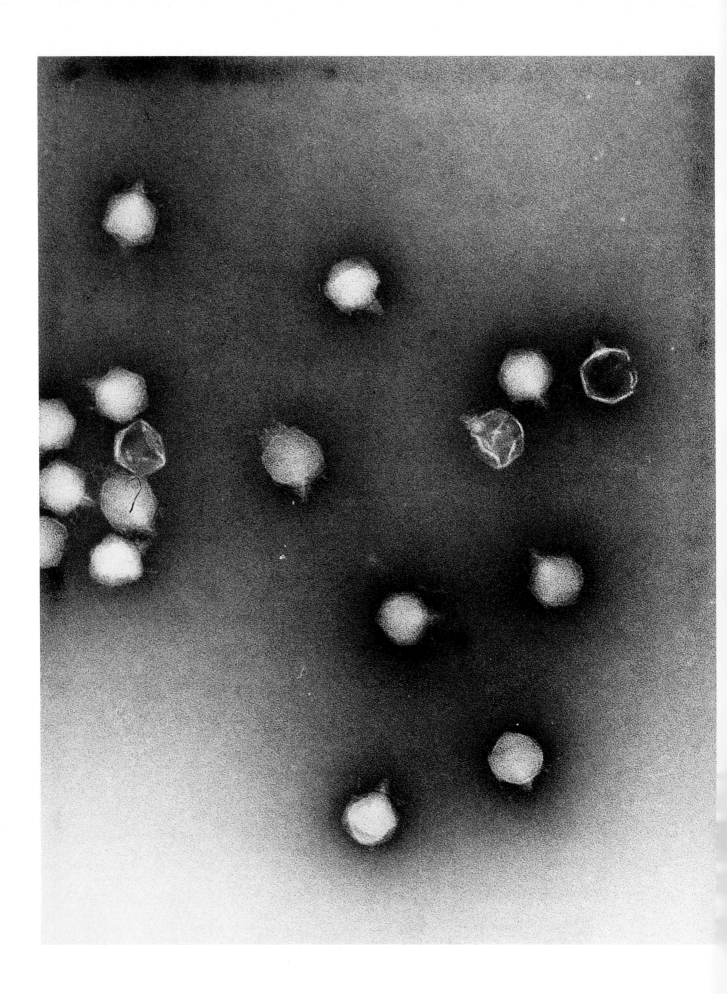

PLATE XXIX   BACTERIOPHAGE T7   x 250,000

DNA, double-stranded, 50 percent

Binal: isometric head (polyhedral) 60 nm, short, conical tail *ca.* 12 × 20 nm, short fibers at tail-head junction

I N 1945 DELBRÜCK designated the original seven strains of bacterial viruses for which *E. coli* is the host as types T1 through T7. Later, these were found to fall essentially into three distinct serological and morphological groups: the T-even group with rigid tails, the T3 and T7 without tails, and T1 and T5 with flexuous tails. Although for some time the T-even group of bacteriophage were the favorite research objects of a very active school of phage workers, many of the unique properties of the type T7 phage, and its close relative T3, have stimulated much interest, partly because they are less complicated structurally than the other members of the series, and partly because of unique features of their nucleic acid.

In the early period of study of the series of T-phages, T3 and T7 were described as spherical and devoid of tails, leading to much speculation on the mechanism of adsorption to the bacterial host. However, with the development of a technique of freeze-drying specimens for electron microscopy with a minimum of distortion of the preparation, they were shown to be hexagonal in outline and to possess short, stubby tails as seen on Plate XXIX. In terms of the molecular biology of self-assembly this small degree of structural complexity places bacteriophage T7 intermediate between the simple viruses, which are helical or icosahedral, and the T-even bacteriophages which have several subassembly steps, in proper sequence, in the construction of the complete virion. Quantitative polyacrylamide gel electrophoresis of purified T7 phage has yielded an estimate of 460 for the number of copies of the major structural protein, with molecular weight 35,000 daltons, along with ten other proteins represented by fewer than a dozen copies each. The total molecular weight of these eleven proteins is 653,000 daltons, an amount of protein requiring more than half of the T7 genome for its coding.

Interesting properties have been found in the biosynthesis of the T7 nucleic acid as well as in its composition. During the intracellular synthesis of the phage DNA a rapidly sedimenting, shear-fragile structure called a concatemer has been identified. When examined in the electron microscope these intermediates in the production of progeny T7 DNA molecules are found to be three to four times the length of the mature molecules. Studies with amber mutants, and with the inhibition by chloramphenicol of the enzymatic scission to mature T7 DNA, have been interpreted as indicating the presence in the long intermediate form of nicks in one strand of the double-stranded DNA, about one phage equivalent unit apart. These would yield, upon scission, one headful of double-stranded DNA with a molecular weight of 25×10^6 daltons.

The base composition of T7 phage DNA also has turned up some interesting properties which have provided a very useful tool in the study of its transcription. Whereas most phage DNA's show pyrimidine clusters of both dC and dT types on both strands, T7 phage DNA is found to be free of the dT-rich clusters and to contain polyG-binding, dC-rich clusters on only one of the two complementary strands. It has been hypothesized that these dC-rich clusters are related to initiation of RNA transcription, and also serve as termination sites. Experiments have shown that essentially 100 percent of the various T7-specific RNA's hybridize with the DNA strand which has the dC-clusters. Thus, it appears that only one (and always the same) strand is transcribed during the growth cycle of this phage.

Selected Bibliography

Adolph, K. W., and Haselkorn, R.: Comparison of the structures of blue-green algal viruses LPP-1M and LPP-2 and bacteriophage T7. *Virology, 47:* 701, 1972.
Carlson, K.: Intracellular fate of deoxyribonucleic acid from T7 bacteriophages. *J Virol, 2:* 1230, 1968.

113

Fraser, D., and Williams, R. C.: Details of frozen-dried T3 and T7 bacteriophages as shown by electron microscopy. *J Bacteriol, 65:* 167, 1953.

Hausmann, R., and LaRue, K.: Variations in sedimentation patterns among deoxyribonucleic acids synthesized after infection of *Escherichia coli* by different amber mutants of bacteriophage T7. *J Virol, 3:* 278, 1969.

Kelly, T. J., Jr., and Thomas, C. A., Jr.: An intermediate in the replication of bacteriophage T7 DNA molecules. *J Mol Biol, 44:* 459, 1969.

Summers, W. C., and Szybalski, W.: Totally asymmetric transcription of coliphage T7 *in vivo:* Correlation with poly G binding sites. *Virology, 34:* 9, 1968.

PLATE XXX

BACTERIOPHAGE LAMBDA (λ)

x 250,000

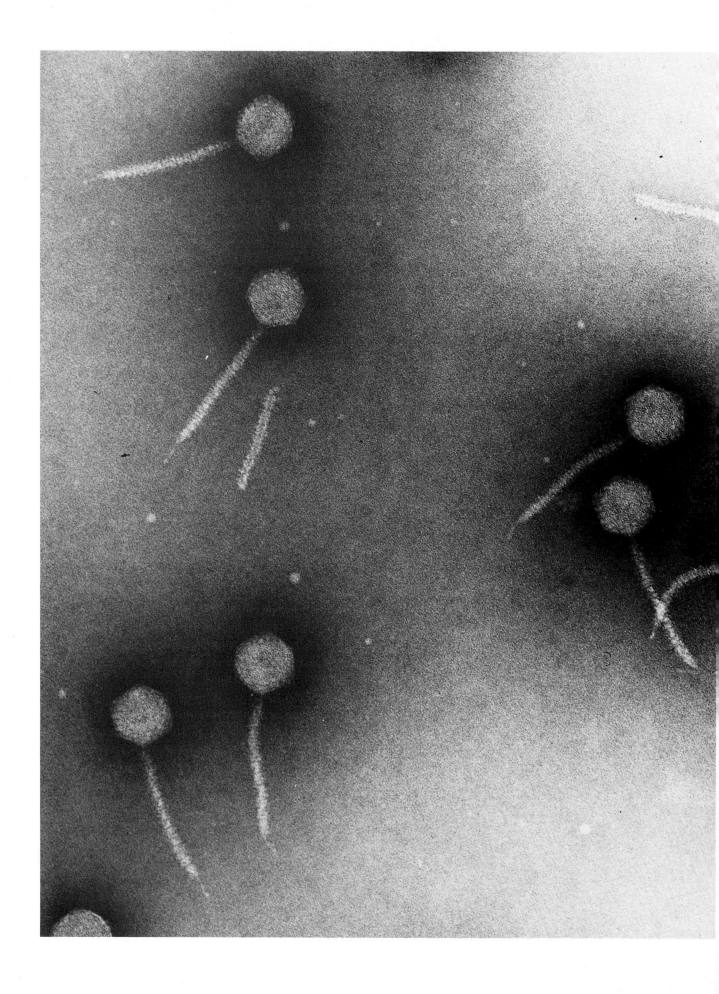

PLATE XXX   BACTERIOPHAGE LAMBDA (λ)   x 250,000

DNA, double-stranded, 50 percent

Binal: isometric head (polyhedral) 55 nm, flexuous tail 15 nm × 160 nm, attached fibers

B Y FAR the most information gathered on any coliphage has been compiled for the bacteriophage lambda. In fact, by 1971 there was sufficient information on this single phage species to justify the publication of an 800 page book. The lambdoid phages, as the members of this recombinant group are called, represent the most widely studied temperate phages that can establish lysogenicity in *E. coli* strain K-12. In infection with a temperate phage, such as λ, one of two possible paths may be taken: first, the more commonly observed lytic response of a virulent infection in which the cell is destroyed after a short latent period; second, a lysogenic response in which the temperate phage genome becomes integrated with that of the cell and the cell is not immediately killed. In the second case, however, the capacity to become induced to the lytic response is maintained indefinitely and is carried along as the cell multiplies. Cells in this condition are said to carry a prophage and are immune to superinfection by λ. Since they have descended from cells which have entered the lysogenic pathway they are called lysogens.

Since there are two separate pathways possible during infection with phage λ there must be two genetic map regions. One region would provide the information for the orderly sequential expression of genes in the lytic pathway for the regulation of phage development, the replication of DNA, and for synthesis of the structural phage proteins necessary before lysis. The other region must include the genes to turn off the lytic sequence and to permit the specific integration of the viral DNA into the host cell DNA at the proper site on the chromosome.

The mechanism by which it is possible to turn off the lytic sequence formed part of the basis for the classical model of gene control by repressors described by Jacob and Monod in 1961. In this elaboration of their operon concept they proposed that the product of a repressor gene (called the CI gene) directly blocked early functions required for DNA synthesis. This same cytoplasmic repressor also was believed to maintain the immunity to superinfection. The inactivation of the repressor by inducing agents, such as ultraviolet light, produced the induction of the prophage to follow the lytic sequence. It was some time, however, before the λ repressor was isolated and shown to be a protein which could specifically bind to the region of the host chromosome known to contain the proper operator. Virtually all of the known λ genes are controlled either directly or indirectly by this repressor.

In addition to turning off the lytic sequence, the lysogenic pathway must have a mechanism to insert or integrate the viral DNA into the host chromosome. A way whereby this insertion might be accomplished was given in a model by Campbell in 1962. This model proposed three steps: (1) circularization of the viral DNA; (2) specific pairing over a region of the host DNA; and (3) a single reciprocal recombination event within this homology region permitting the linear insertion of the viral DNA into the host chromosome.

Observations by many researchers are explained by the above model. For instance, excision of the prophage could occur simply by a reversal of the insertion process, a process thought to explain the origin of transducing phage lines. Upon infection these transducing phage particles transmit to the host cell some segments of the bacterial chromosome which were adjacent to the paired region and thereby give to the new host cell some bacterial genes from the original lysogen. Normal prophage induction is not an exact reversal of insertion, however, since there is evidence that the ends of the bacterial chromosome are not rejoined after excision. The first step of the Campbell model predicts that the phage genes will be circularly permuted and data from genetic methods support this conclusion. Also, the second step in the integration model allows for specific pairing at other attachment sites, leading to the possibility of a low frequency of double lysogens. These strains, containing two prophages per chromosome, are found. The Campbell model predicted the occurrence of intracellular λ DNA molecules in the form of circles some time in advance of their actual demonstration.

The bacteriophage λ DNA molecule is double-stranded with a molecular weight of about 3.2×10^7 daltons, is about 17 μm in length, and has no unusual bases. However, there are several properties of the DNA that have been useful in the correlation of structure and genetic function. Particularly interesting have been the studies of the cohesive ("sticky") ends, the differences in base composition along the length of the DNA molecule, the differences in base composition between the two strands, and the genetic map as revealed by electron microscopy. In a series of experiments in several laboratories, particularly by Hershey, Kaiser, Thomas, Szybalski and their coworkers, it has been found that: (1) when denatured λ DNA is exposed to renaturing conditions, two new species of DNA are formed, both of which sediment more rapidly than the native λ DNA in sucrose gradients; (2) one of the new forms is a circle formed by interaction between cohesive ends at opposite ends of the same molecule; (3) the single-stranded regions have mutually complementary 5'-terminated ends; (4) the single-stranded regions are required for biological activity in a transformation system in which cells are infected both by isolated λ DNA and by a λ *helper* phage with genetic characteristics different from the transforming purified λ DNA; and (5) physical mapping of viral genes can be accomplished by electron microscopic examination of artificially formed heteroduplex molecules. In these physical mapping experiments, combinations were formed by renaturing one strand of DNA purified from a deletion mutant, or from a trans-

ducing phage, with the complementary strand from a normal phage DNA. The unpaired region was revealed as a collapsed single-stranded region and its distance from the ends of the DNA molecule could be measured.

Lysates of cultures infected with λ phage contain normal virions with DNA-filled heads attached to striated tails (Plate XXX) and a smaller form, called petit lambda, which is empty and never attached to a tail. Capsomers can be seen on the head membrane (Figure 17). Analysis by acrylamide gel electrophoresis of normal λ capsids yields two proteins, a major component of molecular weight 45,000 daltons and comprising about 85 percent of the phage protein, and a minor component of 14,000 daltons. The petit capsid, however, contains only the larger protein component, leading to speculation that the minor protein acts as a morphogenetic factor.

Mutants used in the study of the morphogenesis of phage lambda are all controlled by genes located in the left arm of the genome. This genetic region involved in the late functions of the virus maturation is in two major groups. One group of seven genes controls phage head formation, and mutants devoid of these genes produce tails but no head structures. The other group of eleven genes is required for the formation of phage tails. A third, minor group controls polymerization of the head proteins into normal phage capsids;

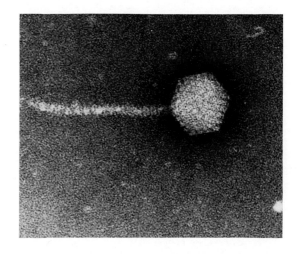

Figure 17. A virion of bacteriophage λ, showing some detail of capsomeric arrangement. ×250,000.

Plate XXX—Bacteriophage Lambda (λ)   119

mutants in this group of genes are found to have tubular heads rather than icosahedral ones. In studies of morphogenesis it has been found that purified λ heads and tails can join *in vitro* to form infectious phage. The initial steps in morphogenesis of the λ head involve maturation and packaging of the DNA molecule within the head membrane protein. Through the action of two additional gene products these heads are subsequently combined with the complete phage tails.

Selected Bibliography

Buchwald, M., Steed-Glaister, P., and Siminovitch, L.: The morphogenesis of bacteriophage lambda. I. Purification and characterization of λ heads and λ tails. *Virology, 42:* 375, 1970.

Campbell, A. M.: Episomes. *Adv Genet, 11:* 101, 1962.

Echols, H., and Joyner, A.: The temperate bacteriophage. In Fraenkel-Conrat, H. (Ed.): *Molecular Basis of Virology,* New York, Reinhold, 1968, pp. 526–575.

Hershey, A. D. (Ed.): *The Bacteriophage Lambda.* New York, Cold Spring Harbor Laboratory, 1971, 792 pp.

Hershey, A. D., Burgi, E., and Ingraham, L.: Cohesion of DNA molecules isolated from phage lambda. *Proc Natl Acad Sci USA, 49:* 748, 1963.

Jacob, F., and Monod, J.: Genetic regulatory mechanisms in the synthesis of proteins. *J Mol Biol, 3:* 318, 1961.

Kaiser, A. D., and Hogness, D. S.: The transformation of *Escherichia coli* with deoxyribonucleic acid isolated from bacteriophage λdg. *J Mol Biol, 2:* 392, 1960.

Lederberg, E. M.: Lysogenicity in *E. coli* K-12. *Genetics, 36:* 560, 1951.

MacHattie, L. A., and Thomas, C. A., Jr.: DNA from bacteriophage lambda: Molecular length and conformation. *Science, 144:* 1142, 1964.

Mathews, C. K.: *Bacteriophage Biochemistry.* New York, Van Nostrand Reinhold, 1971, 373 pp.

Weigle, J.: Assembly of phage lambda *in vitro. Proc Natl Acad Sci USA, 55:* 1462, 1966.

Westmoreland, B. C., Szybalski, W., and Ris, H.: Mapping of deletions and substitutions in heteroduplex DNA molecules of bacteriophage lambda by electron microscopy. *Science, 163:* 1343, 1969.

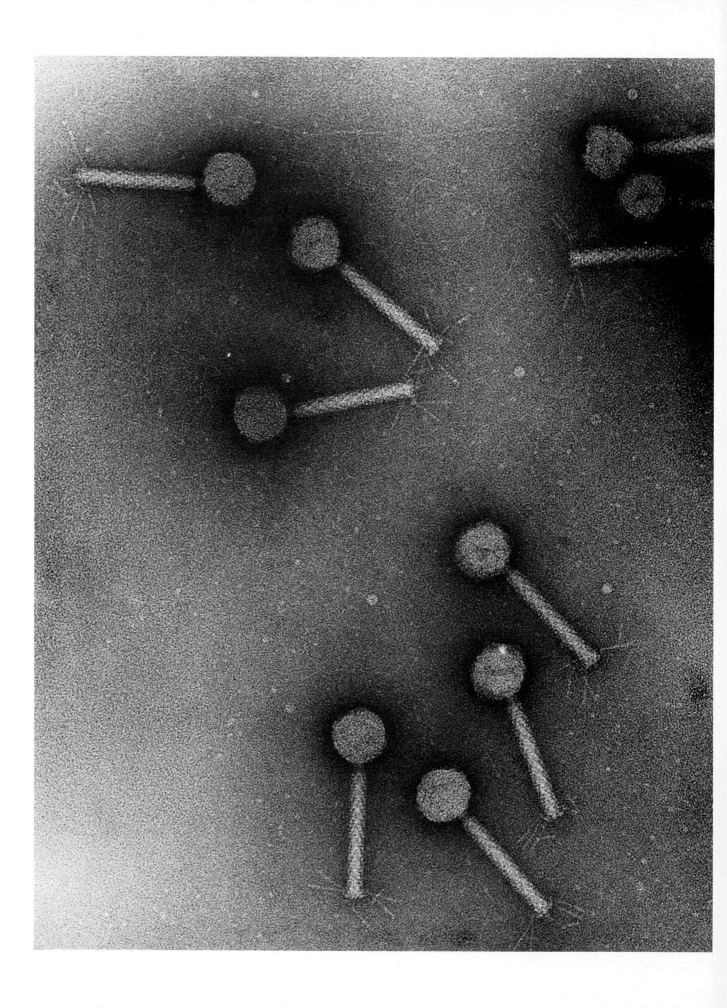

PLATE XXXI   BACTERIOPHAGE P2   x250,000

DNA, double-stranded, 50 percent

Binal: icosahedral head 62 nm, rigid helical tail 18 nm × 135 nm, attached fibers

IN 1950 BERTANI found that the lysogenic *Escherichia coli,* strain "Li," liberated several bacteriophages which were active on a strain of *Shigella dysenteriae.* He classified these phages into three types (P1, P2 and P3) according to plaque morphology and found that they were also serologically distinct, although somewhat cross-reacting, and completely unrelated to any of the T-phages. Bacteriophage P2 was the large plaque type and eventually became the most studied member of an interesting family of temperate phage. Some of the interest in the P2 family stems from the differences between it and the λ family of phages. The elegant and unified hypothesis developed for phage λ (Plate XXX), which explains the important aspects of phage behavior in terms of the regulation of gene activity by means of cytoplasmic repressors, does not exactly apply to P2 because the latter phage is noninducible. This means that P2 cannot be converted, as the lambdoid phages can, from the lysogenic state to a round of viral growth by ultraviolet irradiation or other agents which interfere with nucleic acid metabolism. Proposals for genetic regulation in phage P2 will be considered below.

Along with the obvious structural differences between P2 phage (Plate XXXI) and phage λ (Plate XXX), other differences between these two phages can be identified by the following characteristics: (1) phages of the λ family can recombine genetically with each other, as can the members of the P2 family, but cross recombination between the two families does not occur; (2) the λ family of phages can act as helper phages in the transformation test of Kaiser and Hogness whereas P2 cannot; (3) the cohesive ends of the DNA of the phages within either family will cohere with one another, but there is no reaction between the sticky ends of the DNA of two phages from different

families; (4) phage P2 is not induced by treatments such as ultraviolet irradiation, thymine starvation or addition of mitomycin C, all of which induce phage λ; (5) those treatments which induce phage λ do not cause a loss of immunity in P2 (i.e. host cells are not lysed by superinfection with homologous phage) or production of phage in cells lysogenized by temperate P2; (6) phage P2 are not amenable to zygotic induction; and (7) mutants of P2 with temperature-sensitive immunity cannot be induced by a temperature shift. For these reasons, bacteriophage P2 is considered a noninducible, temperate coliphage distinctly different from λ.

On the P2 phage genetic map the genes with related functions are in most cases grouped together. For instance, the first genes activated to set up the machinery for biosynthesis in virulent growth (the *early* genes), the genes which are activated later for the virion maturation and release (the *late* genes), and the genes which act to preserve the lysogenic state are found in clusters. There are two early genes, A and B, located at the right end of the genetic map which are required for DNA replication and expression of late genes. The product of gene A is unusual and gives positive control over the expression of all other essential genes. Normally the product of a gene is considered freely diffusible in the cell, and when different conditional lethal mutants simultaneously infect the same cell, the protein that cannot be formed by one mutant is available from the other and vice versa (i.e. they can complement each other). The protein product of gene A, however, affects only the chromosome from which it was formed and for this reason it is called *cis*-acting.

The next lettered gene from the right on the P2 map is the immunity gene C, which codes for a protein immunity substance, or repressor.

When there is sufficient repressor to block viral replication the lysogenic state is maintained and genes A and B are not read. This makes the cell immune to superinfection by a homologous phage. It is generally believed that induction in some way can cause the level of a repressor to drop below some critical value and a cycle of lytic growth can begin. Between gene B and immunity gene C several mutations leading to virulence have been found. They probably define the site at which the repressor binds to the P2 DNA, thereby presumably blocking expression of the early genes A and B and preventing transcription of late genes as well.

The model proposed by Campbell for prophage integration and the reverse excision described for phage λ (Plate XXX) should also apply to P2. The former function is known to require a specific product produced by a gene in phage P2 called *int* for integrase. This gene on the P2 map is just to the left of immunity gene C. Experiments by L. E. Bertani have shown that when induction is attempted in P2 it is abortive because the prophage does not detach from the host genome because of a lack of *int*. She proposed that the *int* function of P2 is not controlled by phage repressor (as in λ), but that it is under *split-operon control*. This means that the *int* gene is split or disrupted physically by the prophage integration and its activity would depend on the configuration of the phage chromosome rather than on the presence of phage repressor protein.

Bacteriophage P2 has a satellite phage P4 which can reproduce only with the assistance of a helper genome such as the prophage of P2 in *E. coli* strain C cells. Although the P4 phage appears to contain all of the same structures (head, tail with contractile sheath, and tail fibers) of P2, the diameter of the P4 head is much less than that of P2. The satellite phage P4 is able to direct the synthesis of a head smaller than that of P2 (for a comparison see Figure 18), and yet the heads of both are composed of identical proteins. Apparently the satellite phage requires all of the seven known P2 tail genes and most of the P2 head genes (the late genes) for development, and yet it does not require the early genes, nor does it require the P2

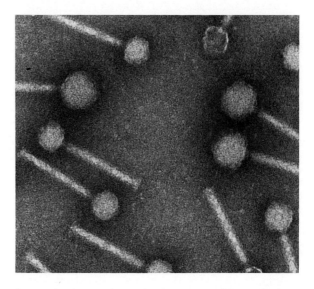

Figure 18. Comparison of appearance of bacteriophages P2 and P4. The latter appears identical with the former, except for its smaller head size. ×160,000.

prophage to detach from the bacterial chromosome and replicate the P2 template. The P4 DNA is unique in base sequence, has cohesive ends and a molecular weight of only 6.7×10^6 daltons, compared to the 2.3×10^7 daltons for P2. Although the physical size of the DNA itself may play a role in determining the head size, the smaller head is a unique result of the presence of the P4 genome and no particles with the head size of P4 are found in cells infected by P2 alone. This relative paucity of the P4 DNA is consistent with its need to have a helper genome in order to undergo a complete lytic growth cycle.

The P2 phage particle has a head that is isometric, and probably icosahedral, with a diameter of about 62 nm. Many virions exhibit a distinct capsomeric arrangement, but the triangulation number, T, of the array has not been established. The protein products of most of the P2 head genes have been examined by electrophoretic migration in SDS-polyacrylamide gels and compared with the capsid proteins. The major capsid protein makes up 90 percent of the total molecular weight. The product of one of the genes is a protein of molecular weight 44,000, which is apparently cleaved to the size of the major capsid protein, of molecular weight 36,000 daltons, while another

Plate XXXI—Bacteriophage P2   123

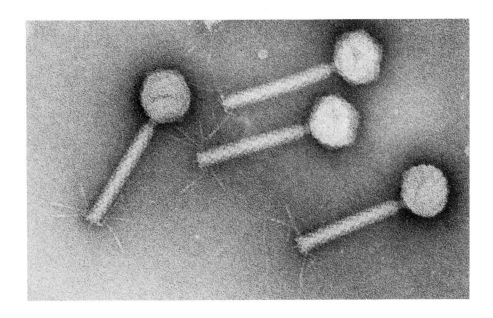

Figure 19. Electron micrograph of bacteriophage P2 in which the six tail fibers are seen on the virion at the left. Three particles show a single spike at the end of the tail. ×185,000.

protein is cleaved concomitantly. Proteolytic cleavage apparently also occurs in the head assembly of some other viruses (T4, λ), and two models have been proposed to explain the role of cleavage. The models differ with respect to whether the cleavage occurs while the nucleic acid is being incorporated into preformed heads, or whether uncleaved protein condenses with the DNA and cleavage then occurs to stabilize the capsid shell irreversibly.

The P2 tail is a cylindrical, rigid structure approximately 135 nm long and 18 nm wide. Attached to the end of the tail are six fibers about 40 to 50 nm in length, while at the end of the inner tail tube is a single spike. The inner tail tube is surrounded by a contractile sheath which presumably operates on injection of the DNA into the host cell in the same way as in the T-even phages. There is a double-disc collar which connects the tail to the phage head, with the terminal disc located inside the head

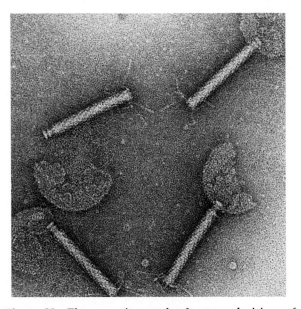

Figure 20. Electron micrograph of ruptured virions of bacteriophage P2. The double-disc collar at the proximal end of the tail is seen; one disc appears to be located within the head membrane, and one is located outside. ×230,000.

membrane and the other disc outside the head membrane. (See Figures 19 and 20 for details of the structure of the P2 tail.)

Selected Bibliography

Bertani, G.: Studies on lysogenesis. I. The mode of phage liberation by lysogenic *Escherichia coli*. *J Bacteriol, 62:* 293, 1951.

Bertani, G.: Lysogeny. *Adv Virus Res, V:* 151, 1958.

Bertani, L. E.: Split-operon control of a prophage gene. *Proc Natl Acad Sci USA, 65:* 331, 1970.

Calendar, R.: The regulation of phage development. *Annu Rev Microbiol, 24:* 241, 1970.

Calendar, R., Lindahl, G., Marsh, M., and Sunshine, M.: Temperature-inducible mutants of P2 phage. *Virology, 47:* 68, 1972.

Inman, R. B., Schnös, M., Simon, L. D., Six, E. W., and Walker, D. H., Jr.: Some morphological properties of P4 bacteriophage and P4 DNA. *Virology, 44:* 67, 1971.

Lengyel, J. A., Goldstein, R. N., Marsh, M., Sunshine, M. G., and Calendar, R.: Bacteriophage P2 head morphogenesis: Cleavage of the major capsid protein. *Virology, 53:* 1, 1973.

Lindahl, G.: Genetic map of bacteriophage P2. *Virology, 39:* 839, 1969.

INDEX

W

Wound Tumor Virus, Plate XIV
  capsomers, 55
  core, 56
  CPV, comparison with, 56
  hosts, 55
  RNA, 56
  tumors, 55

X

X-ray analysis, ix

Y

Yellow fever virus, 67

Z

Zygotic induction, 121